New Inside Out

Philip Kerr & Ceri Jones
Series authors: Sue Kay & Vaughan Jones

Upper intermediate

Workbook

MACMILLAN

Macmillan Education
Between Towns Road, Oxford, OX4 3PP
A division of Macmillan Publishers Limited
Companies and representatives throughout the world

ISBN 978 0 230 00920 2 (with key edition)
ISBN 978 0 230 00921 9 (without key edition)

Text © Philip Kerr, Ceri Jones, Sue Kay and Vaughan Jones 2009
Design and illustration © Macmillan Publishers Limited 2009

First published 2009

Original design by Jackie Hill, 320 Design Limited
Page make-up by Carolyn Gibson
Illustrated by Beach, Martin Chatterton, Ivan Gillet, Jo Goodberry, Peter Harper,
Ed McLachlan and Nicola Slater.
Cover design by Andrew Oliver

The authors would like to thank the editor, Alyson Maskell, for everything she has done.
Once again.

The author and publishers are grateful for permission to reprint the following copyright
material:
Material from article 'What men really want from a holiday' by Guy Browning, copyright
© Guy Browning 2002, first appeared in Eve Magazine August 2002, reprinted by
permission of the author;
Poem 'What Teachers Make, or Objection Overruled, or If things don't work out, you can
always go to law school' by Taylor Mali, copyright © Taylor Mali, reprinted by permission
of the author.

'Magnetism' and 'Three Hours Between Planes' taken from The Cut Glass Bowl by F. Scott
Fitzgerald. Retold by Margaret Tarner. First published in the Macmillan Guided Reader
Series, 1995.

These materials may contain links for third party websites. We have no control over, and
are not responsible for, the contents of such third party websites. Please use care when
accessing them.

The authors and publishers would like to thank the following for permission to reproduce
their photographs:
Alamy/Bubbles Photolibrary p38, Alamy/Peter Casolino p38, Alamy/David Noble
Photography p71 (b), Alamy/Folio p20tl, Alamy/Mike Goldwater p14 (b), Alamy/
Gavin Hellier p14(a), Alamy/Richard Levine p38, Alamy/Picorial Press Ltd p9, Alamy/
Pictorium p10, Alamy/Andy Selinger p71(a), Alamy/Westend61 GmbH p44, Alamy/
Edward. J. Westmacott p27; Corbis/Bettmann p14, Corbis/Image Source p20tr;
Getty Images p51tl, Getty/Jac Depczyt p43, Getty Images/Alan Smith p71 (c), Getty
Images/ Jerome Tisne p48; By kind permission of Oxford University Press p55t; Penguin
Group UK p55m; Random House p55b; Rex Features/ Action Press p22tr, Rex Features
/20thC.FOX/ Everett p32, p63, Rex Features/cMGM/Everett p58, Rex Features/R Watson
p14bl.

Printed and bound in Spain by Edelvives

2012   2011   2010   2009
10 9 8 7 6 5 4 3 2 1

Contents

Impressions

Grammar

1 Match the verb structures with the examples in the text below.

a) Present simple _____1_____

b) Present continuous _____

c) Past simple _____

d) Past continuous _____

e) Present perfect simple _____

f) Present perfect continuous _____

g) Past perfect simple _____

h) Past perfect continuous _____

I (1) *live* in a small flat in London. I (2) *'ve been studying* management and my course (3) *has* almost *finished*. When I (4) *arrived*, I (5) *'d been planning* to look for a job here, but now I (6) *'m thinking* of going to the United States. I (7) *'d* never *wanted* to go there before, but I (8) *wasn't expecting* to find London so expensive.

2 Underline the most appropriate verb form.

I (1) **am just buying / <u>have just bought</u>** a really cool pair of blue sunglasses. I (2) **walked / was walking** around Camden Market when I (3) **have seen / saw** a new designer shop. I (4) **had been looking / used to look** for some Aviator glasses for ages, and the shop (5) **was selling / had sold** some very cheaply. I (6) **used to have / would have** a very similar pair. I (7) **had always been feeling / always feel** so much more comfortable when I (8) **'m wearing / have worn** sunglasses.

3 Complete the pairs of sentences by choosing *So* or *Neither* and filling the gaps with an auxiliary verb. Three of the pairs of sentences are completely untrue! Which ones?

a) Berlin holds an annual film festival.
   So / Neither ___*does*___ Venice.

b) *Star Wars* is one of the most successful films of all time.
   So / Neither _____ *Titanic*.

c) Nicholas Cage has never won an Oscar.
   So / Neither _____ Jodie Foster.

d) The directors of *No Country for Old Men* won an Oscar in 2008.
   So / Neither _____ Daniel Day-Lewis.

e) Angelina Jolie has a famous father.
   So / Neither _____ Kiefer Sutherland.

f) Jennifer Lopez has never got married.
   So / Neither _____ Antonio Banderas.

g) Heath Ledger was not born in America.
   So / Neither _____ Schwarzenegger.

h) Matt Damon trained as a ballet dancer.
   So / Neither _____ Tom Hanks.

4 Write responses to the sentences below that are true for you. Use EITHER a phrase with *so* or *neither*, OR a phrase with *I* + an auxiliary verb.

a) I love Madonna's music.
   So do I. / I don't!

b) I've always wanted to be a film star.
   _____

c) I'd like to have lots and lots of children.
   _____

d) I never watch MTV.
   _____

e) I don't really pride myself on anything.
   _____

f) I'm reading a great book at the moment.
   _____

g) I used to bleach my hair.
   _____

h) I've never seen any of Madonna's films.
   _____

i) I couldn't live without my trainers.
   _____

5 Match the questions with the appropriate tag.

a) You were born in 1991,   are you? ☐
b) You're Canadian,   weren't you? R
c) You aren't married,   can you? ☐
d) You don't smoke,   did you? ☐
e) You've got a car,   didn't you? ☐
f) You lived in Quebec,   do you? ☐
g) You can't swim,   have you? ☐
h) You've never worked,   haven't you? ☐
i) You didn't study Art,   aren't you? ☐

🌐 01 **Listen and check your answers. Then listen again and say if these are real questions (with rising intonation) or if they are asking for agreement (falling intonation). Write R for rising and F for falling intonation in the boxes.**

6 Complete each sentence with a question tag.

a) She has a baby girl, _hasn't she_ ?
b) I didn't promise, _____ ?
c) OK, I forgot to tell you yesterday, but I'm telling you now, _____ ?
d) You've put on a few kilos, _____ ?
e) Her last album wasn't very good, _____ ?
f) She never writes, _____ ?
g) Nobody wants to look like that, _____ ?
h) Let's change the subject, _____ ?

7 Five of the sentences below contain grammatical mistakes. Correct the mistakes and put a tick (✓) below the sentences that are correct.

a) I'd like to know who has made the biggest impression on you.
✓ _____

b) Do you mind tell me how you met him or her?
_____

c) Could you tell what your first thoughts were?
_____

d) Would you say that you knew him or her well?
_____

e) Do you think that you did make a good impression on him or her?
_____

f) Do you know what is he or she doing now?
_____

g) I'd like to know you still have the same opinion about this person.
_____

Write true answers to the questions.

8 Rewrite the questions below, beginning with the words given.

a) What kind of salary are you looking for?
Do you know what _kind of salary you are looking for?_

b) Which political party do you vote for?
Could you tell me _____
_____

c) Do you work well under stress?
Do you think that _____
_____

d) Have you ever been in trouble with the police?
Do you mind telling me _____
_____

e) What is more important for you: money or job satisfaction?
I'd like to know what _____
_____

f) Are you a 'morning-person' or an 'afternoon-person'?
Would you say that _____
_____

g) Do you believe in God?
I'd like to know whether _____
_____

Which of these questions would you answer truthfully at a job interview?

Pronunciation

🌐 02 **Listen to the following mini conversations. In each dialogue, put a tick (✓) next to the speaker (A or B) who sounds more interested.**

a) A: I'm working on a magazine feature about trainers.
B: Trainers? Really?

b) A: I work for the American Central Bank.
B: Oh, do you?

c) A: I'm going to the shops this afternoon.
B: You're not going to Zara, by any chance?

d) A: We went clubbing last night.
B: Again?

e) A: Don't you think she looks just like Gwyneth Paltrow?
B: More like my mum.

f) A: There's football on TV tonight.
B: Oh, great.

Practise the mini conversations. Try to sound as interested as possible.

Vocabulary

1 Put the adjectives into two groups.

abrasive	charming	fake	harsh
hearty	shrill	sparkling	strident	warm

Usually positive characteristics	Usually negative characteristics
_____	_abrasive_
_____	_____
_____	_____
_____	_____
	_____

2 Match the adjectives (*a–g*) with the nouns (*1–7*) to make strong collocations.

a) fake   1 clothes
b) abrasive   2 eyes
c) close-set   3 hair
d) limp   4 handshake
e) scruffy   5 manner
f) shrill   6 smile
g) tousled   7 voice

a	b	c	d	e	f	g
6						

3 Complete the sentences with the words in the box.

charming	designer	forced	hearty
husky	impassive	spiky	staring

a) She had a ___charming___ manner and we felt very welcome.
b) He introduced himself and gave me a _____ handshake.
c) She had an _____ face and it was impossible to know her feelings.
d) He had a _____ smile and I knew he wasn't really happy.
e) She had dark, _____ eyes and I thought she was a little mad.
f) He had _____ hair which was coloured pink and green.
g) She had an attractive _____ voice when she sang.
h) He always wore _____ clothes when he went clubbing.

4 Complete the sentences with the words in the box.

rebuild	reconsider	~~rediscover~~	reinvent
relocate	reschedule	reunite	rewrite

a) I found an old box of CDs last night, so I'm going to ___rediscover___ the music I liked as a child.
b) I hope that one day the two parts of the island will _____ .
c) It took a long time to _____ the hotel after the tsunami.
d) Many pop stars _____ themselves so they can sell their music to a new generation.
e) My company is going to _____ to India, so I need to find another job.
f) She said that she didn't want to get married but I asked her to _____ .
g) The teacher asked me to _____ my essay.
h) They decided to _____ the meeting for a later date.

5 Underline the correct alternative.

a) I'd like to **rearrange** / **repackage** the furniture in the classroom.
b) They managed to **reconsider** / **reconstruct** the economy with help from the World Bank.
c) I'm afraid you're going to have to **rethink** / **reunite** your ideas.
d) I think you should **reinvent** / **reword** your answer so that it's a little more polite.
e) I've heard they're going to **remake** / **reorganise** the film with American actors.
f) My computer crashed and I had to **redo** / **remake** all my work.
g) The prime minister is trying to **relocate** / **repackage** himself as a socialist.
h) It's time to **re-examine** / **redraft** all the evidence and find out exactly what happened.

6 Insert the missing letters to label the parts of clothes.

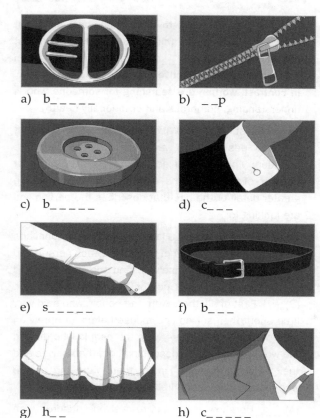

a) b _ _ _ _ _

b) _ _ p

c) b _ _ _ _ _

d) c _ _ _

e) s _ _ _ _ _

f) b _ _ _

g) h _ _

h) c _ _ _ _ _

7 Complete the sentences with words from Exercise 6.

a) It was just an off-the-_cuff_ remark.

b) She's nearly 100 years old but she's still as bright as a _____ .

c) Why does she always _____ me when I think I've finished work for the day?

d) My mother says I'll have to tighten my _____ with all the economic problems these days.

e) You have to admit that she wears her heart on her _____ .

f) It's really time for her to _____ down and do some work.

8 Match the responses below with the sentences in Exercise 7.

1 But she hasn't stopped spending money, has she?

2 Yes, but I think she should hide her feelings for him a little more.

3 Yes, but it's a pity that he didn't think more before opening his mouth.

4 Yes, she seems to think that our time is her time, doesn't she?

5 Yes. Otherwise she'll never pass her exams.

6 Yes, she's very quick, isn't she?

1	2	3	4	5	6
d					

9 Underline the correct word to complete the conversation.

Jack: Hey, you'll never (1) **guess** / **know** / **say** who I saw last week.

Megan: Who?

Jack: Nicole Kidman. She's renting a house in my street.

Megan: No! It (2) **can't** / **mustn't** / **shouldn't** be her. She lives in Australia. You say such stupid things sometimes.

Jack: Calm (3) **about** / **down** / **round** and listen. She's making a movie here in London.

Megan: I don't believe you. You're just trying to (4) **make** / **mind** / **wind** me up.

Jack: No, I'm not. It's true. I spoke to her.

Megan: Stop it! You're so (5) **angry** / **annoying** / **surprising**. I know it's not true.

Jack: OK, OK. But you believed me when I told you about Johnny Depp.

🔘 **03 Listen and check.**

10 Insert the missing letters to complete the conversation.

Megan: Look at (1) t_h a t_ man (2) o _ _ _ there.

Jack: Which one? The (3) o _ _ (4) w _ _ _ the short hair?

Megan: Yes. He's the spitting (5) i _ _ _ _ of Kiefer Sutherland!

Jack: Him? He (6) b _ _ _ _ absolutely no (7) r _ _ _ _ _ _ _ _ _ to Kiefer Sutherland!

Megan: Yes, he does. And look! He's got the (8) s _ _ _ distinctive tattoo on his arm. I'd (9) r _ _ _ _ _ _ _ that tattoo anywhere.

Jack: I'm sorry. I don't think he (10) l _ _ _ _ anything (11) l _ _ _ Kiefer Sutherland.

Megan: Yes, he does. In fact, I think it's him. He's an amazing-(12) l _ _ _ _ _ _ guy, don't you think?

Jack: Well if that's Kiefer Sutherland, he's changed a lot!

Megan: Hey! He's walking towards us! It really is him!

🔘 **04 Listen and check.**

Reading

1 Read the four personal advertisements below. Which two ads do you think will get the most replies?

> **BRUNETTE,** 27, looking for someone kind, romantic, spontaneous, caring, and who is willing to take a risk. We can always tell them we met in the supermarket! *Ref 070901*
>
> **GENUINE,** attractive, outgoing professional female, good sense of humour. Enjoys keeping fit, socialising, music and travel. Would like to meet like-minded, good-natured guy to share quality times. *Ref 070902*
>
> **MALE,** good sense of humour, adventurous, athletic, enjoys cooking, comedy, culture, films, seeks sporty, fun female for chats and possible romantic relationship. *Ref 070903*
>
> **BRIGHT,** fun, gym-loving guy, non-smoker, singer-songwriter, into detective novels, funny films, American comedy shows, and long walks on sunny beaches. Interested? *Ref 070904*

2 Read the article opposite. Were your answers to question 1 correct?

3 Read the article again and insert the sentences (*a–g*) in the spaces (1–6). One sentence does not belong in the article.

a) He then divided his results into three groups.

b) He was interested in the impression that different ads made on the person who was reading them.

c) Many men said that they liked action films, but musicals were more popular with women.

d) Much more popular were the ads that mixed the 'me' and the 'you'.

e) Researchers have studied the question and their results are not surprising.

f) The next job was to discover how people reacted to these different styles.

g) Time and again, they were very wrong about which ads the men would find appealing.

🌐 **05 Listen and check.**

4 Find words in the text to complete the table.

noun	verb	adjective
appeal	_____	_____
attraction	_____	_____
enticement	_____	enticing
temptation	_____	tempting

The *psychology* of personal ads

Imagine that you want to write a personal ad. What choice of words do you think would attract the largest number of replies? (1) ____ Men tend to look for women who are physically attractive, understanding and athletic. In contrast, women are searching for someone who is understanding, humorous and emotionally healthy.

Psychologist Richard Wiseman decided to look at personal ads another way. (2) ____ He asked the question: which type of ad would entice the greatest number of replies – the one that describes you in greater detail or the one that describes the person you are looking for?

To find out, he looked at a large number of personal ads and counted the number of words that each person had used to describe themselves, and the number used to describe the type of person they were looking for. (3) ____ First of all, there were the people who said very little about themselves and focused almost entirely on their wish list. Then there were the people who divided the words more evenly, describing both themselves and their potential partner. Finally, there were the people who focused almost entirely on themselves.

(4) ____ He showed the ads to over one hundred men and women and asked them to say which ones they would reply to. Only a small number of people said that they found the 'it's all about you' ads appealing. The 'it's all about me' ads did a little better, but still didn't tempt many replies. (5) ____ The most successful ads had a balance of 70 per cent 'this is me' and 30 per cent 'this is what I'm looking for'.

The research also provided one very useful piece of advice for anyone who is thinking of writing an ad. For the ads that were written by men, other men were able to predict which ads would appeal to women. But for the ads written by women, it was a different story. (6) ____ So, girls, if you're thinking of putting an ad in the personal columns, get a man to write it for you!

This one looks interesting. Attractive, lonely female, 22, looking for the man who can make me laugh.

Personal Ads

Writing

Writing a short biography
Sentence structure and paragraph organisation
Spelling

1 Read the article and choose the best title.

    a) As tears go by

    b) The life of a hippy

    c) A voice and a life

2 Use the paragraph plan below to put the paragraphs (a–c) in the correct order.

Paragraph 1 ☐

Who is he/she? Age?
What is he/she famous for?
How popular is he/she in your country?

Paragraph 2 ☐

What does he/she look like?
Has he/she ever changed his/her appearance or image?
Do you know what he/she has been doing recently?
What is the best thing he/she has ever done?

Paragraph 3 ☐

When did you first become aware of him/her?
Have you ever seen him/her in real life?
How long have you been a fan?
What do you particularly like about him/her?
Is there anything you don't like about him/her?

3 Divide paragraph (a) into five sentences

4 Ten of the eleven words below are spelt wrongly. Correct them. You can read the text again to check your answers.

apeared	beuatifull	consert	diferent
extremly	fasinating	favrite	includeing
intresting	resently	serious	

5 Write about a famous living person that you like or admire.

You should use the paragraph plan in Exercise 2 to help you.

Make notes before you start writing

You should write approximately 180 words.

a) I first discovered her music because my mother used to like it and listen to it when she was cooking about ten years ago Marianne Faithfull was in concert here and we went together she was superb I love the way she sings and she has had such a fascinating life I don't like everything that she has done but she's always interesting

b) Marianne Faithfull is an English singer and actress who is probably in her 60s now. She is best known for her music and she has recorded with many different artists, including David Bowie and Metallica. She has also appeared in a number of films.

c) Faithfull was extremely beautiful when she was young, and she dressed in the hippy clothes that were the fashion among all her London friends. She looks more serious now, but she is still very good-looking. She has recently released a new album, but she hasn't been doing any concerts because she is unwell. My favourite song of hers is 'As Tears Go By', which she recorded in the 1960s and which was written by Mick Jagger and Keith Richards of The Rolling Stones, and Andrew Oldham, who had 'discovered' Marianne. She was going out with Mick Jagger at the time.

Generations

Grammar

1 Six of the sentences contain a grammatical mistake. Correct the mistakes and put a tick (✓) under the sentences that are correct.

a) Lidia decided to studying in England.
   Lidia decided to study in England.

b) She wanted her parents pay for her studies.
   _____

c) Unfortunately, they could not afford help her.
   _____

d) Lidia found a job and managed to save the money.
   _____

e) She arranged to stay with some family friends in Newcastle.
   _____

f) The family friends didn't ask her pay any rent.
   _____

g) She loved to going to classes and she made lots of friends.
   _____

h) She spent her free time look after the friends' children.
   _____

2 Underline the correct alternative.

a) Stop it! You're **aiming** / **forcing** / <u>**making**</u> me laugh.

b) **Decide** / **Let** / **Offer** me do it for you.

c) I can't **afford** / **force** / **let** you to do it, but …

d) Please! Will you **allow** / **avoid** / **make** me to speak?

e) I hope your parents don't **enjoy** / **get** / **warn** to hear about that!

f) Let's **arrange** / **dread** / **encourage** to meet at the weekend.

g) Don't even **attempt** / **finish** / **urge** to explain! I won't believe you.

h) I don't **aim** / **expect** / **mind** paying.

i) Why didn't you **ask** / **hope** / **try** me to do it?

Have you ever said the sentences above, or has anyone ever said them to you (in your own language)? In what circumstances?

3 Put the verbs in brackets into the correct form.

a) I always try _to understand_ (understand) my parents' point of view.

b) I avoid _____ (talk) to my parents about personal things.

c) I can't stand _____ (go) to big family reunions.

d) I expect my parents _____ (help) me financially all my life.

e) I enjoy _____ (spend) time with my parents' friends.

f) I have never told my parents _____ (leave) me alone.

g) I never let my parents _____ (know) all my secrets.

h) I often ask my parents _____ (give) me advice.

Change the sentences above to make them true for you. Tick (✓) the sentences that are already true.

_____
_____
_____
_____
_____
_____
_____

4 Rewrite the second sentence beginning with the words given, so that it means the same as the first.

a) They didn't have enough money to buy lots of new clothes.

They couldn't afford _to buy lots of new clothes._
_____

b) They told me that it was a good idea to go to church every week.

They encouraged _____
_____

c) They always refused to allow me to bring friends home.

They never let _____
_____

d) They insisted on me coming home at ten o'clock every night.

They made _____
_____

e) They said that I shouldn't go to discos because they were dangerous.

They warned _____
_____

f) My father thought that I should work in his sock factory.

My father expected _____
_____

g) I learned from my parents to respect authority.

My parents taught _____
_____

h) I was really nervous about telling my parents that I had a boyfriend.

I was dreading _____
_____

i) I succeeded in running away from home when I was 15.

I managed _____
_____

j) I made an attempt to live on my own, but it was very hard.

I tried _____
_____

5 Complete the text with the words in the box.

about	~~at~~	at	for	in
of	on	to	to	with

Two years ago I went to a language school in Ireland and stayed with a host family. At the time, I was hopeless (1) ___at___ English and it was difficult (2) _____ understand them very well. But they didn't say much anyway and I had the impression that they weren't very interested (3) _____ me. I was amazed (4) _____ how little they said, even to each other. This was quite surprising, because I thought the Irish were famous (5) _____ being very communicative. I was quite pessimistic (6) _____ my chances of improving my spoken English.

The family were very keen (7) _____ sausages, which we had for dinner almost every day. At least that was better than the boiled fish (which I'm allergic (8) _____) that we had on Fridays. I was afraid (9) _____ saying anything about the food, but one day I'd had enough. The words poured out of my mouth and I was really impressed (10) _____ my progress in English!

6 Write the words in order to complete the questions.

a) difficult find get in it morning the to up ?

Do you _find it difficult to get up in the morning?_

b) embarrassing English for speak to you

Is it _____

c) emails find get irritating it spam to

Do you _____

d) a easy for keep secret to you

Is it _____

e) adverts boring find it on to TV watch

Do you _____

f) amusing at family photos find it look old to

Do you _____

Write true answers to the questions.

Vocabulary

1 Put the words in the box in order, where 1 = the youngest and 6 = the oldest.

adolescence	adulthood	~~infancy~~
middle age	old age	childhood

1   _infancy_

2   _____

3   _____

4   _____

5   _____

6   _____

2 Underline the correct alternative.

a)   I'm **dreading** / **avoiding** my parents finding out my exam results.

b)   She is **aiming** / **arranging** to be a millionaire before she's thirty.

c)   I **afford** / **avoid** having meetings first thing in the morning.

d)   Do you think you will **expect** / **manage** to finish all the work on time?

e)   The manager **urged** / **hoped** his players to attack more in the second half.

f)   Don't do it, OK? You have been **offered** / **warned**!

g)   I don't **mind** / **prefer** doing the washing-up, if you like.

h)   If we want to help her to do well, we should really **decide** / **encourage** her to study more.

3 Write the words in order to make sayings about family and friendship.

a)   at begins charity home
     Charity begins at home.

b)   blood water than thicker is
     _____

c)   heart home is is the where
     _____

d)   a birds feather flock of together
     _____

e)   a company crowd three's two's
     _____

f)   another deserves good one turn
     _____

4 Match the situations (*1–6*) with the sayings (*a–f*) in Exercise 3.

1   After he won the lottery, a lot of Joe's friends asked him to help them in various ways. But Joe decided, first of all, to help his sister set up her own company. ☐ *a*

2   To thank Joe for his generosity, his sister called her company 'My Brother Joe'. ☐

3   Joe wanted to celebrate his lottery win with a quiet evening in a restaurant with his girlfriend. Every few minutes, unfortunately, someone came to his table to talk to him. ☐

4   A few years after becoming a millionaire, Joe found that many of his new friends were also millionaires. ☐

5   Joe bought a luxury apartment in Manhattan, but after a while he decided to go back and live in his small house in the village of Wimbish. ☐

6   Back in his village, he discovered that he got on better with his sister, brothers and cousins than he did with his new millionaire friends. ☐

5 Match the adjectives in the box with the definitions.

allergic	amazed	fed up	hopeless
~~impressed~~	irritating	optimistic	

a)   admiring someone or something very much
     impressed

b)   annoyed or bored with something that you feel you have accepted for too long
     _____

c)   making you feel annoyed or impatient
     _____

d)   not skilful at all
     _____

e)   thinking that good things will happen in the future
     _____

f)   unable to eat something for medical reasons
     _____

g)   very surprised
     _____

6 **Complete the sentences with adjectives from Exercise 5.**

a) Don't ask me to mend the car! I'm absolutely ___hopeless___ at anything mechanical!

b) Don't cook fish for him – he's _____ to it.

c) I thought I'd done very badly in the exam, but I got 94%. I was _____ at how well I'd done.

d) It was an excellent film. I was really _____ with the acting.

e) Let's be _____ about our chances. It'll all be OK.

f) Please stop singing that song. I find it really _____ to have to listen to it twenty times a day.

g) I'm completely _____ with work. I need a new challenge.

7 **Complete the conversation with the words in the box.**

call	have	help	make	shout
show	~~take~~	welcome		

Penny: Hello, you must be Cedric. Come in, come in. Let me (1) ___take___ your bag.

Cedric: Thanks. That's very kind of you, Mrs Hoskins.

Penny: Oh, you must (2) _____ me Penny! Did you (3) _____ a pleasant trip?

Cedric: Not too bad, thanks.

Penny: Glad to hear it. Anyway, (4) _____ to our home. Come into the living room and (5) _____ yourself comfortable.

Cedric: Thank you, Mrs Hoskins.

Penny: Amanda will be home soon, but before she comes, I'll (6) _____ you around. You'll be in the room next to Amanda's.

Cedric: Oh, right, thanks.

Penny: I'll just go and make us a nice cup of tea. And, here, (7) _____ yourself to the biscuits.

Cedric: Thanks.

Penny: If there's anything you need while I'm in the kitchen, just give me a (8) _____ .

Cedric: OK, Mrs Hoskins. Thanks.

🌐 **06 Listen and check.**

8 **Insert the missing letters.**

a) I know the room isn't v_ _ _ big, but make yourself at home.

b) I hope you don't m_ _ _ the dog.

c) E_ _ _ _ _ the mess.

d) I'm a_ _ _ _ _ the TV is broken.

e) S_ _ _ _ about the painting.

Pronunciation

1 **Put the words in the box in the correct spaces.**

annoy	~~chase~~	cheers	clothes	clown
fake	flight	ground	hair	host	join
parent	serious	wild		

a) /eɪ/ grey, say, ___chase___ , _____

b) /aɪ/ buy, try, _____ , _____

c) /ɔɪ/ boy, toy, _____ , _____

d) /əʊ/ go, know, _____ , _____

e) /aʊ/ how, now, _____ , _____

f) /eə/ their, where, _____ , _____

g) /ɪə/ hear, near, _____ , _____

🌐 **07 Listen and check. Repeat the words.**

2 **Underline the word in each group that has a different vowel sound.**

a) host   lost   most

b) near   wear   year

c) five   give   wives

d) how   low   now

e) gave   have   save

🌐 **08 Listen and check.**

Listening

1 🌐 09 **Cover the listening script opposite. Listen and look at the pictures of three women when they were 21 years old. Match the speakers (1–3) to the pictures.**

Lalita Parikh, 43, has a 21-year-old daughter, Akhila

Christine Rance, 56, has a 21-year-old daughter, Leia

Mary Billups, 65, has a 21-year-old step-daughter, Zoë

Speaker 1: picture	_____
Speaker 2: picture	_____
Speaker 3: picture	_____

2 **Listen again and tick the topics that each speaker mentions. Some topics are mentioned by more than one speaker.**

	Speaker		
topic	**1**	**2**	**3**
boyfriends			
entertainment			
fashion			
marriage			
money			
music			
politics			
studies			
work			

1 When I was my step-daughter's age, I remember my own parents saying to me all the time 'You've never had it so good', but I could never quite understand what was so good about it. There was the music – the Beatles and the Rolling Stones – and the new fashions, mini-skirts of course, but they didn't really change much for most of us. I got a job when I left school, a real dead-end job it was, too. I was working in a horrible office, nine-to-five, or more like eight-to-six, and in the evenings we had dinner and watched TV – black and white, of course. I'd done a three-month secretarial course and I never had the chance to go to college like my step-daughter. I think she's lucky. The sixties weren't all they're cracked up to be! She has so much more freedom than I ever had. I'm not complaining, but I wish I'd been born twenty years later. Who knows how my life would have been different?

2 When I was my daughter's age, things were very different. We didn't spend all our time shopping or watching rubbish on TV like my daughter and her friends seem to do all the time. I mean, don't get me wrong, I love my daughter, but she doesn't seem to care about anything that matters. I suppose the world was very different then. It was still the days of the Cold War and we were much more political. Most weekends, we were at demonstrations. South Africa was still run by the apartheid regime, General Pinochet was still in charge in Chile and there were wars just about everywhere. The world was in a real state. Mind you, I'm not so sure that things are a lot better now. Kids these days have it so easy. I mean, they have so much money and everything is handed to them on a plate.

3 When I was my daughter's age, I hadn't been in England long. Perhaps for a little more than a year. Actually, I came over here to get married and the first few years it was hard to make ends meet, with my husband trying to set up his business. Basically, I was spending many days with my husband's family, but when our daughter came along, there was not time for very much. Now that she is grown up, we would like her to meet a nice boy and get married, right? We sometimes suggest first-class boys that she will like, but she is not interested. She has finished her studies at the Middlesex University and she says that she wants to have her career. Obviously, we want her to have the best of both worlds, work and family, but we worry that she will wait too long before she settles down.

3 **Find the idioms (a–f) in the listening script and underline the best definition.**

a) a dead-end job (Speaker 1)
   a bad job / a good job

b) not all they're cracked up to be (Speaker 1)
   not as bad as people claim / not as good as people claim

c) in a real state (Speaker 2)
   in a very bad way / in a very good way

d) handed to them on a plate (Speaker 2)
   made very easy for them / made very hard for them

e) make ends meet (Speaker 3)
   get a job / survive financially

f) the best of both worlds (Speaker 3)
   a situation where two cultures meet / a situation where you have two very different advantages

Writing

1 **Complete the emails below using the phrases a–n opposite.**

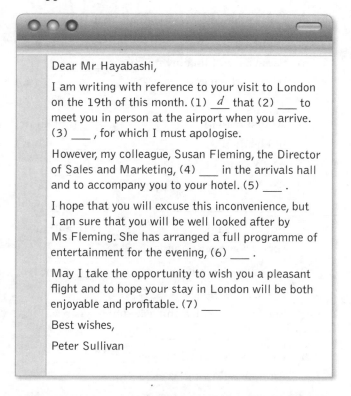

Dear Mr Hayabashi,

I am writing with reference to your visit to London on the 19th of this month. (1) _d_ that (2) ___ to meet you in person at the airport when you arrive. (3) ___ , for which I must apologise.

However, my colleague, Susan Fleming, the Director of Sales and Marketing, (4) ___ in the arrivals hall and to accompany you to your hotel. (5) ___ .

I hope that you will excuse this inconvenience, but I am sure that you will be well looked after by Ms Fleming. She has arranged a full programme of entertainment for the evening, (6) ___ .

May I take the opportunity to wish you a pleasant flight and to hope your stay in London will be both enjoyable and profitable. (7) ___

Best wishes,

Peter Sullivan

Hi Petra,

How are things? Are you still planning to come and stay with us later this month? I'm really looking forward to seeing you again and catching up on all your news.

Anyway, the reason I'm writing is that (8) ___ , so (9) ___ to come to the airport to meet you. (10) ___ about that.

Not to worry, though. Maddie, one of the girls I share a flat with, has said that she (11) ___ . She'll be waiting for you when you come through the arrivals gate. She's got long blond hair and she'll be carrying a red umbrella. (12) ___ .

I won't get back from the work trip till the next morning, but Maddie will look after you. She's got tickets for the Cold Play gig, (13) ___ . (14) ___ .

Love,
Minty

a) 'll come to the airport to pick you up
b) but if you don't fancy that, she'll go along with whatever you want to do.
c) I look forward to seeing you again at our meeting on the 20th.
d) I sincerely regret
e) I will be unable
f) I won't be able
g) I'm really sorry
h) See you on Tuesday morning!
i) She will be holding a board with your name.
j) She's got a photo of you so she knows what you look like.
k) should you wish to take advantage of it.
l) something's come up at work
m) This is due to work commitments
n) will be there to welcome you

2 **Shortly after receiving these emails, Mr Hayabashi and Petra learn that the time of their flight has been changed. The plane will now arrive at London Airport at 15.00, three hours earlier than planned.**

Look at the phrases below and write H if they come from Mr Hayabashi's reply or P if they come from Petra's reply.

a) All your old friends send their love. _P_
b) I am sorry to hear that you will not be available. ___
c) Thank you for your email concerning my arrival in London. ___
d) I hope that the change to my schedule will not cause her any problems. ___
e) I hope this will be OK. ___
f) I would be grateful if you could confirm the new arrangements. ___
g) Is your boss giving you grief? ___
h) Thanks for your letter about meeting me at the airport. ___

3 **Now write two short emails, one from Mr Hayabashi to Peter Sullivan, and one from Petra to Minty. In the letters, explain about the change in arrival time and apologise for any inconvenience.**

3 Gold

Grammar

1 **Underline the correct verb form.**

a) 'I'm going abroad.'
He said he **was going** / **went** abroad.

b) 'We'll see you later.'
They said they **would see** / **saw** us later .

c) 'Did you have a good time?'
We asked them if **had they had** / **they had had** a good time.

d) 'I can't come tomorrow.'
She said she couldn't come **the next day** / **the previous day**.

e) 'I haven't finished.'
She explained that she **didn't finish** / **hadn't finished**.

f) 'I'd love to come.'
He said he **would love** / **had loved** to come.

g) 'We went to bed late.'
They told us they **'d go** / **'d gone** to bed late.

h) 'Are you going to have an early night?'
She asked me if **we were going** / **were we going** to have an early night.

2 **Read the conversation and complete the reported speech sentences at the top of the next column using the verbs in brackets. You may need to add the personal pronouns *he*, *she* or *they*.**

Chris : Guess what? I've just won the lottery.

Sarah: How much did you win?

Chris: 10,000 pounds!

Sarah: What are you going to do with it?

Chris: I don't know! I think I'll buy a new car, for a start.

Sarah: That'll take most of the money, won't it?

Chris: Yeah, but I want to keep a little bit to spend on a holiday.

Sarah: A holiday?

Chris: Yeah, do you fancy coming to the Maldives?

Sarah: Wow! The Maldives! I'd love to! When are we going?

Chris: What are you doing next week?

a) Chris phoned Sarah to tell her that _he had just won_ (just/win) the lottery.

b) Sarah asked him how much _____ (win) and what _____ (do) with it.

c) At first he said _____ (not know) but he thought _____ (buy) a new car.

d) Sarah told him that buying a car _____ (take) most of the money.

e) But Chris said _____ (want) to spend some on a holiday.

f) He asked Sarah if _____ (fancy) going with him.

g) She loved the idea and asked him when _____ (go).

h) Chris asked her what _____ (do) the following week.

3 **Write what the people said.**

a) Chris told Sarah he'd got the tickets.
'I've got the tickets.'

b) Sarah asked if she could see them.

_____

c) Sarah asked when they were leaving.

_____

d) Chris said she had two days to get ready.

_____

e) Sarah asked if she needed to take any money.

_____

f) Chris said that he would pay for everything.

_____

g) Sarah said she was going to buy some new clothes.

_____

h) She asked him if he wanted to go with her.

_____

i) He said that he'd wait for her at home.

_____

4 Correct the mistake in each of these sentences. Ignore the italics.

        was

a) If I ~~am~~ the president of my country, I'd spend more money on *the environment*.

b) If I did ever had the chance, I'd *take a year off and go travelling*.

c) If I could live anywhere in the world, I'd probably bought *a beach villa in Tahiti*.

d) If I didn't need to *learn English*, I would stop a long time ago.

e) If I didn't have to *go to work tomorrow*, I would have stayed at home.

f) If I had been good at *Maths*, I would have *study it at university*.

g) If I was doing more *exercise* when I was younger, I would be *a lot fitter* now.

h) If I'd been born with very rich parents, I wouldn't *doing this job*.

Change the words in italics to make the sentences true for you.

5 Match the *if* clauses (*a–h*) with the correct main clauses (*1–8*).

a) If I wasn't working tomorrow,

b) If I hadn't been so intent on getting rich,

c) If you had saved up like me,

d) If you'd studied a bit more,

e) If you'd been listening more carefully,

f) If you just had a go at it,

g) If I'd taken a bit more care,

h) If you hadn't taken a few risks,

1 you wouldn't have made your fortune.

2 I would have found a lot more happiness.

3 you wouldn't be worrying about the exams.

4 I wouldn't have lost it.

5 I'm sure you'd love it.

6 you wouldn't have wasted your time answering the wrong question.

7 you'd be able to afford it.

8 I'd love to come out, but I need an early night.

a	b	c	d	e	f	g	h
8							

6 Make one conditional sentence with *if* by joining the pairs of sentences.

a) I didn't study hard enough at school. I haven't got a good job.

If I'd studied harder at school, I'd have a better job.

b) It's not made of real gold. It's not worth a lot.

_____

_____

c) They cornered the market. So they put up the price.

_____

_____

d) He has a talent for seeing a gap in the market. He has made millions.

_____

_____

e) She didn't realise it was valuable. She gave it away.

_____

_____

f) My time is so precious. That's why I didn't speak to them.

_____

_____

g) I was working late. I missed the film.

_____

_____

h) I didn't know you were coming. That's why I didn't come to meet you.

_____

_____

Vocabulary

1 **Cross out the noun in each group which is *not* used with the verb in bold.**

a) **have**   a chat, a duty, ~~office~~

b) **make**   a right, a loss, a mess

c) **take**   office, a fortune, responsibility

d) **have**   a look, difficulty, action

e) **make**   sense, a risk, a fuss

f) **take**   way, sugar, an exam

2 **Complete the sentences using *have, make* or *take* in the correct form.**

a) The Californian gold rush __*took*__ place in 1849.

b) Thousands of people find it very hard to _____ a living.

c) Why don't you _____ your father's advice and find yourself a part-time job?

d) If you want to _____ money you have to be ready to _____ risks.

e) I need to _____ a think before I accept your offer. Can I get back to you tomorrow?

f) Oh, come on, there's no need to get angry. We were only _____ a laugh.

g) Don't panic. Don't look down, just _____ a deep breath and then jump.

h) Small businesses often struggle to _____ a profit in the first years.

3 **Complete the sentences using a noun that begins with the letter given.**

a) Steve asked me to have a w __*ord*___ with you about the new offices.

b) If we don't take a_____ now to save our parks and countryside, it may be too late.

c) You can make a f_____ on the internet if you know what to do.

d) Excuse me, could you make w_____ please? The ambulance needs to get through.

e) The company has been making a l_____ for the last six months and it may have to close down.

f) The course is great fun and I don't even have to take an e_____ at the end!

g) Isn't it working? Let me have a l_____ . Maybe I can fix it.

h) Banks have a d_____ to look after their customers' money.

4 **Match the two halves of the expressions.**

a)	a half-baked	1	couple of minutes
b)	a steady stream	2	your while
c)	digest	3	your time
d)	food	4	more profitably
e)	spare a	5	idea
f)	spend the	6	for thought
g)	trickle	7	the information
h)	use your time	8	evening
i)	waste	9	of people
j)	worth	10	slowly

a	b	c	d	e	f	g	h	i	j
5									

5 **Match the expressions in Exercise 4 with the metaphors below.**

a) ideas = food

   _a 5_   _____   _____

b) movement = water

   _____   _____

c) time = money

   _____   _____   _____   _____   _____

6 **Use the expressions in Exercise 4 to complete the sentences below. You may need to make some changes to the verbs.**

a) There was __*a steady stream of people*__ coming in through the gates of the park.

b) The situation was very complicated and it took quite some time for me to
   _____ .

c) You're going to have to learn to
   _____
   or you'll find yourself failing all your exams.

d) The opening speech was very powerful and gave us all a lot of _____ .

e) Do you think my plan could possibly work or is it just _____ ?

f) Excuse me, do you think you could
   _____ ?

g) We _____
   watching old DVDs and eating popcorn.

h) We sat and watched the rain _____
   _____ down the window.

i) If you think you're going to persuade me to take up judo, you're _____ !

j) Can you sit down and help me with this exercise? I'll make it _____ !

7 Complete the texts with the words in the boxes.

blow
breadwinner
living
~~loaded~~
overdraft
peanuts
a rainy day
splash out

A: I wish I was (1) _____ loaded _____ . I'd
    (2) _____ on all kinds of things:
    clothes, shoes, eating out, going on holiday. If
    I didn't have a family to look after and a home
    to run, I'd love to just (3) _____
    all my money on a round-the-world trip, or
    something. But as it is, I have to work hard just
    to earn a basic (4) _____ for me
    and my family. It's really difficult these days,
    being the main (5) _____ .
    My husband works part-time when he can. He
    works for a truck company, but they pay him
    (6) _____ . Some months we
    manage to put a bit of money in the bank, you
    know, saving for (7) _____ ,
    but most of it goes towards paying off our
    (8) _____ – that and feeding
    eight mouths!

boat
budget
hard
made
pricey
range
stretch
worth

B: It isn't (1) _____ much. You know, he isn't
    (2) _____ of money. I know he wanted to buy
    something a little bit more (3) _____ , but he's
    a bit (4) _____ up at the moment and a real
    diamond would have been way out of his price
    (5) _____ . And anyway, we want to spend a
    bit more on the wedding itself, you know, push
    the (6) _____ out, have a big party, invite all
    our family and friends. We haven't got a huge
    (7) _____ , but I think we can (8) _____
    to a buffet lunch and some champagne. After all,
    you only get married once, don't you?

🌐 **10 Listen and check.**

8 Write the words in order to make sentences.

a) looking for colourful was I slightly
   more something
   I was looking for something slightly more
   colourful.

b) wondering have something less you a
   little formal was if I might
   _____
   _____

c) thinking more was something exciting
   I of slightly
   _____
   _____

d) something I a little hoping less was
   for expensive
   _____
   _____

e) older slightly I'd looks like that
   something
   _____
   _____

f) prefer more I'd fun something a little
   _____
   _____

Pronunciation

1 Put the words in the box in the appropriate space.

deluge   special   stretch   treasure
wealthy   whether

a) /θ/ thought   _____
b) /ð/ although   _____
c) /ʒ/ decision   _____
d) /ʃ/ collection _____
e) /tʃ/ rich   _____
f) /dʒ/ range   _____

🌐 **11 Listen and check. Repeat the words.**

2 🌐 **12 Look at the underlined letters, listen to the recording and write the correct symbol.**

a) fortune, future   _____
b) genuine, village   _____
c) decision, disillusion _____
d) theft, worth   _____
e) direction, precious   _____
f) breathe, rather   _____

Reading

1 🌐 **13 Read the article and answer these questions.**

a) How did Peter Huszcz make a million?

_____

b) How long did it take him?

_____

c) What can other inventors learn from him?

_____

_____

2 **Read the article again and match the summaries (a–f) with the paragraphs (1–6).**

a) a summary of his success ☐ 5

b) a description of his first real marketing success ☐

c) a word of encouragement for other inventors who are interested in trying their luck ☐

d) how he first thought of his money-making idea ☐

e) a description of the basic qualities that Peter needed to become a millionaire ☐

f) a description of how he made a start and who helped him ☐

3 **Read the article again and say if the statements are true (T) or false (F).**

a) Peter Huszcz was born to Polish parents in Canada. ☐ F

b) He worked as a waiter in a restaurant in Ottawa. ☐

c) He was good at making meatballs by hand. ☐

d) He thought he was wasting his time making meatballs. ☐

e) The other meatball makers on the market weren't efficient enough. ☐

f) Peter's invention was complex but very efficient. ☐

g) His meatball maker was an immediate success. ☐

h) A TV shopping channel persuaded Peter to let them sell his invention. ☐

i) The meatball maker is very popular in the USA. ☐

4 **Find words in the article that mean:**

a) business person (para 1)

b) someone who knows how to do something very well (para 2)

c) the first example of a new invention (para 2)

d) an attitude that makes you continue trying to achieve something difficult (para 3)

e) showed something on television (para 4)

Meatball Magic:
How to make your first million

So what's the connection between meatballs and big money?

Read the story about Peter Huszcz and find out!

1 Polish entrepreneur, Peter Huszcz, worked as a lecturer in an agricultural college before moving to Canada in the 1990s. But his background in engineering and an unfailing belief that he could make a success of his life drove him on to become a meatball millionaire.

2 He started out washing dishes in a restaurant in downtown Ottawa, and when the manager asked him to help out rolling meatballs in the kitchen, he soon became an expert. But the job was boring and Peter suggested that the manager should buy a meatball-making machine so that Peter could use his time more profitably doing something else. When the manager told him there was no such thing as an automatic meatball maker, Peter was quick to spot the gap in the market. Putting his engineering knowledge to good use, he immediately started work on a prototype. He quickly came up with an incredibly simple but efficient method – the Magic Meatball Maker.

3 He was sure there was a market for his invention, but it took him ten years of hard work and perseverance to find it. He had to take risks, but he believed in his idea, and he managed to persuade other people to believe in him too. A local manufacturer offered to produce the first 1000 units in return for a share in the profits, local shops offered to stock his meatball makers and a friend's daughter helped him out with his first sales.

4 But his lucky break came when he managed to persuade a TV shopping channel to promote the Magic Meatball Maker. The channel aired a simple demonstration of the invention at work in the studio kitchen. Within minutes, they had sold more than 4000 units.

5 This was just the start. Peter had been right. He had said his meatball maker would make him a fortune, and it has: more than two million dollars so far and it's still selling to thousands of American housewives all across the USA.

6 So, to all you potential inventors out there: don't give up. Your idea could be the next million-dollar success so long as you're ready to have a go, take a couple of risks and believe in your dream!

Writing

1 Read the story and circle the best linkers. Sometimes more than one is possible.

On Christmas Eve Mrs Clare was doing some last-minute shopping in her local market (1) **as / until / when** she walked past a stall selling lottery tickets. She decided to buy one for her son. It was getting late, so, (2) **as soon as / before / while** she'd bought the ticket, she rushed home to wrap her presents and put them under the Christmas tree. (3) **As / During / While** she was wrapping her son's present, she slipped the lottery ticket into the bag. And (4) **after / then / when** she forgot all about it. On Christmas Day, her son and daughter-in-law came to her house. They all sat around the tree and opened their presents. Mrs Clare had <u>totally</u> forgotten about the lottery ticket and (5) **after / as soon as / during** her son had opened his present and thanked his mum, he threw the wrapping paper in the bin.

A few days later, Mrs Clare and her son, Jack, were having coffee together in town. (6) **Before / When / While** they were talking, a story came on the local news. It said that the winning ticket for the Christmas lottery had been sold in their local market. <u>Apparently</u> no-one had claimed the winnings.

'Look,' said Bob, 'that's the stall where you usually buy your tickets. And the winning number is the same as my birthday!' <u>Suddenly</u> Mrs Clare remembered her son's second Christmas present. 'Oh no!' she cried, jumping out of her seat.

She explained what had happened to her son and (7) **during / until / while** the endless journey home on the bus, the two tried to remember what they had done with the wrapping. (8) **As soon as / Just as / When** they got home, Mrs Clare and Bob ran to the paper recycling bin and <u>frantically</u> started emptying it, checking every single piece of wrapping paper, (9) **as / before / until**, <u>finally</u>, they found it: the winning ticket!

2 Look at the underlined words in the story. Find replacements for them in the box.

> at last   completely   desperately
> it seemed   just then

3 Look at the pictures below. They tell another story of a lucky lottery ticket. Write the story. Use about 180 words. Use the words in the box to help you. Remember to use appropriate time linkers and adverbs.

> petrol station   glove compartment   papers
> new owner   cheque   champagne

Three months later

4 Challenge

Grammar

1 Underline the correct verb form.

a) I **had always wanted** / **was always wanting** to visit Antarctica since I was a young boy and **saw** / **was seeing** a film about it in school.

b) We **had prepared** / **had been preparing** for the trip for over three months. I was so disappointed when they **cancelled** / **were cancelling** it.

c) We **were getting** / **had got** ready to leave when the phone **rang** / **was ringing** and Phil **told** / **was telling** us the terrible news: someone **stole** / **had stolen** our boat!

d) I **was waiting** / **had been waiting** for this moment for so long. But now that it **finally arrived** / **had finally arrived**, I **didn't know** / **hadn't known** what to do!

e) I **didn't ever do** / **had never done** anything like that before.

f) When my turn **came** / **had come**, I **just closed** / **was just closing** my eyes and **jumped** / **was jumping**.

2 Correct the grammatical mistakes in five of the sentences below. Tick (✓) the sentences that are correct.

a) John was walking home one night. ✓
b) He was hearing a strange noise behind him.
c) It sounded as if someone had followed him.
d) He turned round quickly to see who it was.
e) The noise stopped and John kept walking.
f) He had never been feeling so scared in his whole life.
g) Whoever it was, they had been following him for some time.
h) John hadn't known what to do.
i) He was taking one last look over his shoulder.
j) Then he ran home as fast as he could.

3 Add ten missing auxiliary verbs (*had, hadn't* or *was*) to the text. The first one has been done for you.

Aron Ralston ⎰*had*⎱ been climbing in a remote canyon in Arizona when disaster struck. He climbing down a particularly narrow part when a huge rock fell and trapped his arm. As he been climbing on his own, there was no-one to help him. And he knew that no-one would think of looking for him there because he told anyone where he going. He brought his phone with him, so he couldn't call for help. He waited for five long days, but no-one came to find him. By the fifth day he lost all sensation in his arm. He realised that he had no choice. He would have to cut his arm off at the elbow in order to save his life. Once he cut off his arm, he managed to climb to the floor of the canyon. As he walking out of the canyon, he met a group of people who been hiking in the area. They called for help and a helicopter soon arrived to take him to a nearby hospital.

🌐 **14 Listen and check.**

4 Write the words in order to complete the questions.

a) Aron had when doing happened accident been the ?
What _had Aron been doing when the accident_
happened?

b) him for come hadn't look anyone to ?
Why _____

c) help called he for hadn't ?
Why _____

d) canyon had long he waited in the ?
How _____
_____

e) to done away he had get ?
What _____

f) hikers met doing when he had been the he ?
What _____
_____

5 Answer the questions in Exercise 4. Use full sentences.

a) _He had been climbing in a remote canyon._
b) _____
_____
c) _____
_____
d) _____
e) _____
f) _____

6 Underline the correct verb form.

a) I'll **be finishing** / **have finished** this page *before I go to bed.*

b) I'll **be going** / **have gone** out with friends *on Thursday night.*

c) I'll **be working** / **have worked** hard *all weekend.*

d) I'll **be having** / **have had** my dinner *by the time you get home.*

e) I'll **be getting** / **have got** a new job *by this time next month.*

f) I won't **be going** / **have gone** away on holiday again *for at least six months.*

g) I won't **be doing** / **have done** any sport *this evening.*

h) I'll **be getting** / **have got** married and **having** / **had** three kids *by the time I'm thirty.*

Change the words in italics to make the sentences true for you.

7 Complete the text using the future continuous or the future perfect form of the verb in brackets.

I can see a lot of hard work in the future and you (1) _____ will be doing _____ (do) a lot of travelling in your job. But it'll be worth it. By the time you're twenty-five you (2) _____ (start) your own company. By the time you're thirty you (3) _____ (make) your first million. And you (4) _____ (fall) in love at least three times. The third time will be the real thing. In fifteen years' time you (5) _____ (give up) your job and you (6) _____ (live) in a big house is the country. You (7) _____ (change) your lifestyle completely. You and your husband (8) _____ (run) a small farm and looking after your five children.

🌐 **15 Listen and check.**

Pronunciation

1 🌐 **16 Listen to the recording and underline the word in italics that is more stressed.**

a) I definitely don't *feel up to* it.

b) You'll soon *shake it off.*

c) I think I'm *coming down with* something.

d) The children *wore me out.*

e) The smell really *put me off.*

f) My son looks very like my husband, but he *doesn't take after him* in other ways.

2 🌐 **17 Listen and practise saying the sentences below. Put the stress on the underlined words.**

a) I'm going to cut <u>down</u> a bit on going out.

b) I can't do <u>without</u> you!

c) I can't keep <u>up</u> with all my work.

d) Why don't you come <u>up</u> with a better idea?

e) Let's put it <u>off</u> till tomorrow.

Vocabulary

1 **Complete the sentences with the words in the box.**

deal	genuine	~~imminent~~	interest
obscenely	particularly	shambolic	

a) The team prepared themselves for their
_____imminent_____ departure to the
North Pole.

b) The whole trip was incredibly badly organised
– _____ , in fact.

c) The expedition created a huge amount of media
_____ .

d) The leaders of the expeditions were offered a
very generous book _____ on
their return.

e) It is my _____ belief that anyone
who risks their life for a sport is completely
mad.

f) Only the _____ rich can afford to
have a private jet.

g) He's a _____ gifted pianist.

2 **Complete the sentences with the correct form of
the word in brackets.**

a) She was very _____self-conscious_____ and hated
speaking in public. (conscious)

b) The trip had been very _____ .
Everyone had had a good time. (enjoy)

c) The food was very good and the price was fairly
_____ . (reason)

d) It takes a lot of _____ to give up
smoking. (discipline)

e) He suffers from very low _____ .
He just doesn't believe in himself. (esteem)

f) The government wants to make adult education
more _____ to people who work
full-time. (access)

g) He used to work as a _____
builder before he became an Arctic explorer.
(employ)

h) The stress was getting _____ , so
she left her job. (bear)

i) The key to success is self-belief. If you believe
something is _____ , then you will
achieve it. (achieve)

j) It'll take some organising, but I think it's
_____ . (do)

3 **Match the definitions with the words you wrote in
Exercise 2.**

a) the ability to control your behaviour so that you
do what you should do _____self-discipline_____

b) the feeling that you are as important as
other people and deserve to be treated well
_____

c) gives you pleasure _____

d) possible for you to do (two words)
_____ ; _____

e) so extreme that you can't deal with it
_____ .

f) not too expensive _____

g) easy to get or use _____

h) embarrassed or worried about how you look or
what people think of you _____

i) working for yourself _____

4 **Complete the expressions with the words in the
box.**

out	into	no	~~of~~	jammed
slow	undo	load		

a) in charge _____of_____ : having control over
someone/something and responsible for them

b) the gun _____ : the gun didn't work

c) _____ way: used for emphasising that
something isn't true or possible

d) figure _____ : be able to understand or
solve a problem

e) go into _____ motion: appear to move
more slowly than in real life

f) _____ the gun: put bullets into the gun

g) swing _____ action: start doing something
quickly and efficiently

h) _____ the zip: open the zip

5 **Use expressions from Exercise 4 to complete the
text below. Make any necessary changes.**

He heard a strange noise outside the tent. He lay
there trying to (1) _____figure out_____ what it
was, then he slowly (2) _____ of
the tent door. He quietly (3) _____
and pointed it at the darkness. He was
(4) _____ the camp that night and
there was (5) _____ he was going to
let someone steal their food or equipment. Suddenly
a dark shadow jumped out of the trees: it was a
lion. He quickly (6) _____ . He tried
to fire his gun, but (7) _____ .
Everything seemed to (8) _____ .
He picked up a stick and started shouting wildly.
The lion stopped, looked at him and then turned to
go away.

🌐 **18 Listen and check.**

6 Put the sentences in the right order.

Get fit – you owe it to yourself!

a) walk? Or how about getting a bike and cycling

b) all those extra calories. Or what about doing

c) Are you feeling tired, stressed and out of

d) fresh air. You don't have to get an expensive gym

e) lycra. Try an outdoor option. If you're stuck

f) shape? Then it's time you got out in the

g) inside all day at your job, why not go for a brisk

h) to work and back every day? That'll soon burn off

i) membership to keep fit, or wear

j) some team sports? It's far more motivating – and much more fun.

1	2	3	4	5	6	7	8	9	10
c									

7 Underline the correct verb.

a) I don't really <u>feel</u> / **keep** up to doing any exercise today. Can we leave it till tomorrow?

b) Jamie's incredible, he **gives** / **picks** things up so quickly. He learnt to surf in a day!

c) I'm really trying hard to **give** / **pick** up chocolate. I eat far too much and it's really bad for me.

d) He walked out of the door on to the street and **felt** / **lit** up his last cigarette.

e) What does this mean?
I don't know. **Look** / **Take** it up in a dictionary!

f) Hey, can you slow down a bit, please? I can't **come** / **keep** up with you! You're running too fast.

g) Quick! I need to **come** / **take** up with a good excuse for not playing football tonight!

h) Have you ever thought about **giving** / **taking** up a new sport?

8 Write the words in bold in the correct order.

a) I'm not feeling very well. I think I'm **down coming with** something. _coming down with_

b) Don't laugh! You're **off me putting**. I can't concentrate. _____

c) I'm getting really fed up with this cold. I've been trying to **off it shake** for weeks.
_____

d) Have you seen Jim's dad? He really **him after takes**. They look exactly alike.
_____

e) I'm really sorry, I forgot all about the tennis match. I didn't mean to **you down let.**
_____

f) Give her time. She'll **over get it** soon enough.
_____

g) Yes, that's quite a mystery. We'll have to **into look it.** _____

h) I've tried giving up, but I really don't think I can **it without do.** _____

9 Write the words in order to make sentences.

a) happens   when   horrible   that   It's
It's horrible when that happens.

b) right   serves   you   It
_____

c) blame   got   You've   yourself   only   to
_____

d) home   were   if   go   I   you   I'd
_____

e) death   look   You   like   up   warmed
_____

10 Complete the mini conversations with expressions from Exercise 9.

Conversation 1

A: Oh, my feet! These new shoes are killing me!

B: Oh, I know, (1) _It's horrible when that happens_ . The same thing happened to me last week.

C: (2) _____ .
Those shoes are far too high for walking around town all day!

Conversation 2

A: Are you OK? (3) _____

B: I think it's something I've eaten …

A: (4) _____

B: Yes, I think I will.

Conversation 3

A: Oh, my eyes are really sore.

B: I'm not surprised! (5) _____
_____ . You've done nothing but watch TV for the last five hours!

Listening

1 🔵 19 **Kandi Wright is a snake handler. She is trying to break a world record for living in a cage with 40 poisonous snakes. Cover the listening script opposite and listen to an interview with Kandi and answer the questions.**

a) Why is she doing it?

b) What does she say is the most difficult thing about the experience?

c) Does she get bored?

d) Does she think she'll be able to break the record?

2 **Listen again. Decide if the sentences are true (*T*) or false (*F*).**

a) A man in Zimbabwe had recently succeeded in breaking the record. [T]

b) Her friend suggested that Kandi should try to break the record too. [ ]

c) Kandi has been in the snake cage for more than two months. [ ]

d) She doesn't get a lot of visitors. [ ]

e) A snake bit her on her hand. [ ]

f) She finds it really hard to keep fit. [ ]

g) She spends a lot of time working on her computer. [ ]

h) She's looking forward to getting out of the cage. [ ]

3 **Match the verbs on the left with their collocations on the right.**

a) do   an idea
b) give someone   a new record
c) go   money
d) keep   for a walk
e) raise   fit
f) set   some exercise

Check your answers in the script.

Interviewer: So, Kandi, what gave you the idea for the record attempt in the first place?

Kandi: Well, it all started as a bit of a joke. A friend said she'd seen something on the internet about a man in Zimbabwe who'd set a new record for living in a box with 40 poisonous snakes to raise money for a children's charity. We all thought he must have been mad. But then I started thinking about it, and the idea grew on me. I thought, I could do that – I could break his record. It'd be a great way to raise the profile of Marlton Wildlife Park – you know – get a bit of media interest. So I suggested it – and well, here I am! Day 75 with another 45 to go!

Interviewer: So, how's it been so far? What's been the most difficult thing to get used to?

Kandi: Well, obviously I'm a snake handler – that's my job – so it wasn't difficult getting used to the snakes, but it *was* difficult getting used to the confined space of my 'box' – not being able to go out, not being able to go for a walk, not being able to go back to the comfort of my home at night.

Interviewer: So what do you do all day? How do you keep yourself from getting bored?

Kandi: Bored? I never get the time! I get heaps of visitors – schoolkids, tourists, that kind of thing. I show them the snakes, we talk through this open window here. And then there's the snake page on the park's website – that keeps me really busy. People write in with loads of questions about the snakes – what they eat, where they sleep, if I've been bitten.

Interviewer: And have you?

Kandi: No – not yet! But I did step on one of the mambas one day – poor thing. It was so scared it bit my boot – luckily it's a very strong boot, so its teeth didn't get through to my foot – but I learnt to be more careful about where I put my feet after that!

Interviewer: You look like you're in pretty good shape. How do you keep fit in here? Do you get to do any exercise?

Kandi: Yeah, sure. I've got a running machine in the corner over there. I spend an hour on it in the morning and another 40 minutes or so every evening. It's never been so easy to keep to a fitness regime!

Interviewer: So, what are your plans for the next 45 days? Do you think you'll be able to make it?

Kandi: Sure, no problem. It's just a question of time – and of concentrating on now and not the future – on what I'm doing now and not what I'll be doing when I get out! That just makes the wait seem that much longer!

Interviewer: Well, thanks for talking to us, Kandi, and good luck with the next 45 days.

Writing

Writing an article
Giving advice

1 Read the article and choose the best title.

a) Choosing a marathon

b) Marathons for beginners

c) How to run a marathon

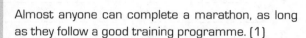

Almost anyone can complete a marathon, as long as they follow a good training programme. [1]

Start by gathering as much information as you can. Try reading books about marathons, surfing the net and talking to people who have already completed a marathon. It's important to find out as much as you can about different training schedules and really think about how that training will affect your life. [2]

Next, you should choose the date and location of your first marathon. [3] It's a good idea to choose a race where other beginners will be taking part. Remember to give yourself plenty of time to train and get ready. Six months is the minimum training period.

Before you start training, you definitely ought to consider investing in a good pair of running shoes. Getting running shoes that are suitable for your running style, foot type, and level of experience will help you run more comfortably and avoid injuries. [4]

As part of your marathon training, it's definitely worth trying out a few shorter races. [5] This is important because there are many new experiences that races bring that regular training does not.

One of the best ways to motivate yourself is to find a running partner. [6] Or maybe you could post a message on this site and find another keen marathon beginner in your area!

2 Find the places (1–6) in the text where the following sentences should go.

a) Think about the time of year you'll be running and the weather. ☐

b) Why not sign up for a 5 or 10 kilometre race? ☐

c) You just need to take the time to find the right training programme for you. ☐

d) Light, comfortable running clothes are equally important. ☐

e) If none of your friends are interested, you could always join a running club near you. ☐

f) And remember to be honest with yourself about whether you can do what is needed. ☐

3 Read the article and the sentences in Exercise 2 again and underline any useful expressions for giving advice.

4 You are going to write a similar article for the same website called 'What to do on the day of the race'. Here are some ideas. Can you think of ways to develop them or add ideas of your own?

1 get up early – give yourself plenty of time to get ready

_____

_____

2 have a good breakfast – at least an hour before running

_____

_____

3 get to the start in plenty of time – you will need to pick up your race number.

_____

_____

4 warm up with a gentle jog or short run – don't do too much or you'll be tired before you start

_____

_____

5 don't worry about the time it takes – just think about finishing

_____

_____

6 enjoy! finishing your first marathon is a great achievement

_____

_____

5 Now write the article. Use approximately 180 words.

5 Ritual

Grammar

1 **Change the verbs in bold into the present simple where possible.**

I've got a really boring report to write this weekend, and I know what'll happen. The same thing that always happens. I (1) **'ll find** all kinds of little tasks to distract me. I (2) **'ll decide** that it's the perfect time to write all those emails to long lost friends, or I (3) **'ll clear** out the inbox on my mobile phone. And I'm sure this time (4) **will be** no different. I (5) **probably won't get** down to work today until I've cleaned the house from top to bottom. Sometimes, when I'm feeling really stressed, I (6) **'ll do** some cooking. At other times I (7) **'ll spend** ages just staring out of the window. Like today. Oh well, I'd better stop wasting time I suppose, or this report (8) **will never get** written!

2 **Write three sentences using *will* describing the kind of things you do to waste time.**

a) _____

_____

b) _____

_____

c) _____

_____

3 **Complete the text with *used to* or *didn't use to*.**

Weddings (1) _____ used to _____ be much simpler in my day. People (2) _____ spend so much money on them for a start. And they certainly (3) _____ go abroad to get married. They (4) _____ get married in the local church and then they (5) _____ invite the guests to a very simple reception afterwards. They (6) _____ have a cake, of course, and possibly some speeches, but they (7) _____ party into the early hours of the morning as they do today. I (8) _____ like the simple, old-fashioned weddings much more.

4 **Look at the text in Exercise 3 again. Where is it possible to replace *used to / didn't used to* with *would/wouldn't*?**

1 ___not possible___   5 _____
2 ___wouldn't___   6 _____
3 _____   7 _____
4 _____   8 _____

5 **Look at the pictures and write sentences about David Hanlon as a young man using the word in brackets and a verb from the box. Three should include *used to*, three *didn't use to*, and three *would*.**

be	be	drink	go	have
like	sing	smoke	wear	

a) (beer) *He used to drink beer.* _____
b) (beard) _____
c) (hippy) _____
d) (discos) _____
e) (champagne) _____

_____

f) (businessman) _____

_____

g) (cigarettes) _____

_____

h) (pony-tail) _____

_____

i) (mobile phone) _____

_____

6 Complete this conversation between two friends with an appropriate form of the verb in brackets. Use *will* or *would* whenever possible.

Jayne: Do you remember Bill? He (1) _used to be_ (be) a real terror in school. Do you remember how he (2) _____ (chase) the girls in the playground? And what about the day when he (3) _____ (find) a frog and (4) _____ (try) to put it down the back of your shirt?

Becky: Yes, of course I do, how could I forget! And, he and his mates (5) _____ (smoke) behind the toilets and they (6) _____ (always / get) caught by the headmaster ...

Jayne: Yeah, and they (7) _____ (have to) do extra homework for a week!

Becky: So what made you bring him up in the conversation?

Jayne: Well, I (8) _____ (see) him a couple of months ago in a café and we (9) _____ (have) a drink and a chat. He hasn't changed that much. He still tells terrible jokes, but, to be fair to him, he (10) _____ (always /pay) for the drinks ...

Becky: 'Always' you say?

Jayne: Yeah, we've been seeing quite a lot of each other. We usually go to the cinema once or twice a week, and sometimes we (11) _____ (have) a game of squash or tennis.

Becky: Mmm ... is it getting serious?

Jayne: I'm not sure. You can judge for yourself. He's joining us later!

🌐 20 Listen and check.

7 Correct the mistakes in six of the sentences below. Tick (✓) the sentences that are correct.

a) Could you remember locking the door on your way out this morning, please?
   Could you remember to lock the door...

b) Do you remember to tell me that I was the only person in your life?
   _____

c) I bet you forgot to bring the money, didn't you?
   _____

d) It's so long ago that I've completely forgotten to say that. Did I really?
   _____

e) She didn't stop insulting me all evening.
   _____

f) They stopped for a minute getting some money out at the bank on the way to the cinema.
   _____

g) This season, I'm going to try winning both the 100 and 200 metres.
   _____

h) Try to cook it in oil – it'll taste a lot better.
   _____

Pronunciation

1 🌐 21 Listen and repeat the phrases below. Make sure that you stress the underlined words.
a) let's <u>face</u> it
b) as for <u>me</u>
c) to be <u>honest</u>
d) it makes me <u>sick</u>
e) <u>here</u> it is

2 Underline one word that is normally stressed in the phrases below.
a) just the two of us
b) it gets on my nerves
c) I can't be bothered
d) it's all in the mind
e) from what I can understand
f) it drives me mad

🌐 22 Listen and check.

Vocabulary

1 Complete the texts with the words in the box.

> came across   derive   immune   ~~jinx~~
> loopy   outfit   renowned   rituals
> striding   upper hand

a) I'm not usually superstitious, but you know how sometimes you feel like you've got a (1) _____jinx_____ – you know, you feel like everything's going wrong? Like today, for example. I was (2) _____ confidently down the street on my way to work. I was feeling good in a new (3) _____ that I was wearing for the first time. Then a car drove right through a big puddle and splashed me with dirty water from head to foot.

b) Most people's superstitions (4) _____ from a basic insecurity: from a need to be in control and to have the (5) _____ in difficult situations. Many (6) _____ sportsmen have personal (7) _____ that they must perform before a big match. Not even politicians are (8) _____ from superstition. One leading British politician admitted to always wearing odd socks on election day. He asked us not to give his name in case he (9) _____ as being a bit (10) _____ !

2 Insert the missing letters.

a) I settled down on the sofa with a mug of hot chocolate and a c o <u>s y</u> blanket.

b) I felt a sudden u _ _ _ to get up and sing.

c) He was furious. He strode out of the room and s _ _ _ _ ed the door behind him.

d) He reached into his pocket, took out a box of m _ _ _ _ _ _ and lit the candle.

e) He passed his driving test on his f _ _ _ _ go.

f) I'm sorry, we have a rule about d _ _ _ _ _ _ _ animals – strictly no pets allowed.

g) Her husband worked in the R _ _ _ _ Air Force and was often away from home.

h) He took the corner at b _ _ _ _ _ _ _ _ speed and almost came off his bike.

3 Write the words in the correct order.

a) bike my go like you to on Would a have
   Would you like to have a go on my bike?

b) surfing go have like at kite I'd a to
   _____

c) all go drink you that Did one really in ?
   _____

d) day all go You've on been the
   _____

e) just go you Why a give don't it ?
   _____

f) best it make He go to tried his a of
   _____

4 Match the expressions (*a–f*) in Exercise 3 with what the speaker said next (*1–6*).

f	1 But it just didn't work.
	2 Sit down and put your feet up.
	3 You can borrow my helmet too, if you want.
	4 You've got nothing to lose.
	5 It looks really exciting.
	6 I can't believe it!

5 Replace the words and expressions in bold (*1–8*) with the words and expressions in the box.

> ~~apt~~   gone for   happy couple   pronounced
> run through   service   sunglasses   walked

'I'm not sure black is the most (1) **suitable** _____apt_____ colour for a wedding,' my mum said as I left the house. But I'd been to the (2) **practice** _____ the night before, and I knew that black wasn't going to be a problem.

The bride had (3) **chosen** _____ a black and white dress and she looked absolutely stunning. Her dad, who (4) **accompanied** _____ her down the aisle, was a little more traditional. He was wearing a pure white linen suit.

The (5) **ceremony** _____ was very moving. The music was great and the (6) **bride and groom** _____ really did look incredibly happy.

I cried when the priest (7) **declared** _____ them man and wife. I always get emotional in weddings. I put my (8) **shades** _____ on so no-one would notice.

🌀 23 **Listen and check.**

6 Find the words in the ring and write them next to the definitions below.

(ring contains: moonreceptionricespeechvow aislebestmanbridesmaidgroomcakeceremonyconfettihoney)

a) formal part of a wedding ____ceremony____
b) party after the wedding _____
c) holiday after the wedding _____
d) man who accompanies the man getting married _____
e) man who is getting married _____
f) formal talk at the wedding reception _____
g) passage in the middle of the church _____
h) promise _____
i) small pieces of paper that are thrown at a wedding _____
j) sometimes this is thrown instead of paper _____
k) this is cut at the reception _____
l) young girl who accompanies the woman getting married _____

7 Underline the correct form of the verb. In one sentence both verbs may be correct.

a) I really feel like I deserve **doing** / <u>to do</u> something special this weekend – I've been working so hard all week.
b) If I can manage **getting** / **to get** the day off on Monday, I could go away for a couple of days.
c) I fancy **going** / **to go** away somewhere – Paris, maybe.
d) I like **visiting** / **to visit** new places and I've never been to Paris before.
e) I'd like **going** / **to go** by train.
f) I enjoy **being** / **to be** able to see the countryside.
g) I can't stand **flying** / **to fly**. I hate airports and all the queuing and waiting around.
h) There'll be probably be lots of extra work waiting for me when I get back. But I don't intend **getting** / **to get** stressed about it now!
i) All I want **doing** / **to do** is take it easy and relax.

8 Complete the sentences with the words in the box.

| ~~complaining~~ go insist keeps on telling |

I share an office with a woman who is forever
(1) _complaining_! When she arrives in the morning,
she'll (2) _____ on opening all the windows
and then she'll (3) _____ on about how cold
it is! She (4) _____ leaving half-finished
cups of coffee on the desk but then she'll go
(5) _____ at me if I knock them over. She's
always (6) _____ me what to do but she
never seems to get on with any work herself!

🔘 **24 Listen and check.**

9 Write the words in order to complete the sentences.

a) what people tell to me do when it
I hate _it when people tell me what to do._
b) shout when me people annoys
It really _____
_____
c) desk most annoys messy me is that a
The thing _____
_____
d) waiting it keep stand people me when
I can't _____
_____
e) nobody irritating listens me when to it
I find _____
_____
f) nerves get manners my on really
Bad _____
_____
g) weekend rains annoying so when it the at
It's _____
_____
h) drive mad some people makes me
The way _____
_____

Reading

1 🌐 25 **Read the film reviews and answer the questions.**

a) Which film do you think would be

 1 the most fun to watch?

 _____

 2 the most romantic?

 _____

 3 the most serious?

 _____

b) Which film does the photo come from?

 _____

2 **Read the reviews again and complete the sentences with the names of the films.**

a) The films *Rachel Getting Married* and _____ are about a relationship between two sisters.

b) _____ is about the relationship between a daughter and her mother.

c) The films _____ and _____ focus on one wedding.

d) _____ shows a number of weddings.

e) _____ and _____ are about secrets.

f) _____ is about two people falling in love.

3 **Find the words (a–h) in the text and match them with the words with similar meanings (1–8).**

a) theme ⬚ `7`
b) extravaganza ⬚
c) soundtrack ⬚
d) edge ⬚
e) gathered ⬚
f) idyllic ⬚
g) mood ⬚
h) fascinated by ⬚

1 atmosphere
2 celebration
3 come together
4 interested in
5 music
6 side
7 subject
8 wonderful

Happily ever after ...

Three films, one theme. Although fewer and fewer people are choosing to get married these days, it seems that more and more films are being made about weddings. Here are our top three wedding movies.

Mamma Mia

The film is set on the tiny Greek island of Laokairi. Twenty-year-old Sophie is planning her wedding and wants her father to be there to give her away. The only problem is that she doesn't know who her father is. She only knows that he could be one of three men: Sam, Harry or Bill. Without letting her mother know, she invites all three men to the wedding, hoping to find out which one is her father. But it's not quite that simple! The film is a fun-filled musical extravaganza, led by Meryl Streep as Sophie's mother Donna, and played against a background of beautiful blue skies and seas and the soundtrack of everyone's favourite Abba songs.

Rachel Getting Married

Rachel Getting Married has a much darker edge to it. It is a comedy, and it is based on a wedding, but the humour is much blacker and the story is far more dramatic. Rachel Buchman has planned the perfect wedding. Friends and family have gathered at their country home in Connecticut and the scene is set for an idyllic, romantic celebration of love. But then Rachel's younger sister, Kym, arrives and the mood changes. Kym has just left a drug-rehabilitation centre and her return to the family home exposes the drama and tragedies behind the happy faces of the wedding guests.

27 Dresses

The 27 dresses in the title are the 27 bridesmaid dresses that Jane has collected from the 27 weddings she has helped to arrange. This is a classic story of 'always the bridesmaid, never the bride'. Jane is secretly in love with her boss, but her boss is far more interested in her younger sister, Tess. In fact, a few weeks after the two first meet, they decide to get married and who else should they ask to arrange the wedding but Jane. A cynical news reporter, Kevin, arrives on the scene. He's fascinated by Jane's bridesmaid obsession and decides to write a story about her. But things get complicated as both Jane and Kevin change their attitudes to marriage.

Writing

Writing a letter of complaint
Formal expressions

1 **Put the letter in the correct order.**

a) Dear Mr Gammack,

b) Further to our telephone conversation, you are aware that over forty of our guests suffered food poisoning, caused directly by the food you provided, and had to be hospitalised.

c) I am writing in connection with the catering services which you provided on 27th October for my daughter, Benita Molly Shepherd's wedding.

d) To add insult to injury, on my way to the hospital, I was presented, by one of your staff, with a bill which was £12,000 over the agreed price. In the circumstances I think my reaction was understandable. I also think a court of law would agree with me.

e) Having taken all of the above into consideration, I have now spoken with my solicitors. You will be hearing from them in due course.

f) Your staff, furthermore, were clearly untrained and unsuitable for this type of work. They provoked a fight when the ambulance arrived, as a result of which my son-in-law, Mr Vinnie Wiseman, was later arrested.

g) Yours sincerely,
Stephen Shepherd

2 **Find and underline phrases in the letter that mean the same as the following.**

a) with reference to

b) as a direct result of

c) above the sum in the contract

d) when the time is right

e) moreover

f) inappropriate for the job

3 **Complete the sentences with a phrase from the box.**

| apology | a full refund | I will expect |
| legal advice | the matter | your life |

a) If I do not hear from you within ten days, I will be obliged to take _____ on this matter.

b) I look forward to receiving _____ as soon as possible.

c) I trust that we will be able to settle _____ amicably.

d) I look forward to receiving a letter of _____ .

e) _____ substantial compensation and a full apology.

4 **You work in the complaints department of a small company. Put the sentences above in order from most threatening to least threatening.**

5 **Imagine you are the father of the bride in the story below. The wedding was cancelled because of the problems with the hire car and the chauffeur. Write your letter to the manager of Limo Car Hire.**

I said 2.30 not 3.30!

6 Eat

Grammar

1 Change the present perfect continuous to the present perfect simple in the four sentences where this is necessary. Tick the sentences that are correct.

a) I've just been listening to the radio. ✓

b) I've always been hating fish.

c) I've been being a vegetarian for about ten days.

d) I've been feeling a bit tired for the last few days.

e) I've been forgetting the names of some students in my class.

f) I've been having the same phone for years.

g) I've been studying English for five years.

h) I've been looking forward to finishing this exercise.

Change the sentences to make them true for you.

2 Look at the picture and put the verbs in brackets into the present perfect simple or the present perfect continuous.

a) They *'ve finished* (finish) work for the evening.

b) I'm pretty sure they _____ (cook).

c) They _____ (have) two accidents in the kitchen.

d) The one with the moustache _____ (eat) spaghetti.

e) They _____ (probably receive) a few complaints from the customers.

f) Two of them _____ (smoke). In the kitchen!

g) I think they _____ (talk) about what went wrong.

3 Correct one mistake in each paragraph.

a) Helen has been working for the government for the last six months. She ~~has~~ got the job by replying to an advertisement online. She's already met the Prime Minister twice.

b) Cedric has been not studying much recently. He failed three exams at the end of last year. He's only been to school three or four times since then.

c) Julie has been going out with Jeff for nearly a year. They met in a café in the centre of town. She didn't tell her parents yet.

d) Alyson has painting her house. She started last month but she hasn't made much progress yet.

e) Hugo has been living with his father for about five months. His parents separated and he has only saw his mother a few times since then.

f) Dan and Ursula have been get ready for their wedding. They announced the date three years ago. They've almost finished their preparations.

4 Put the verbs in brackets into the simple past, the present perfect simple or the present perfect continuous.

Jane: You're looking happy. What's up?

Dick: Well, you know, I (1) *'ve been working* (work) part-time in the evenings at the Red Hot Burger …

Jane: Yes, that's right. You (2) _____ (do) that for about four weeks now.

Dick: Yeah, it was about a month ago that I (3) _____ (start). Anyway, guess what?

Jane: What? You (4) _____ (be paid)?

Dick: Yes, I (5) _____ (be paid) yesterday actually. But, no, it's not that. I (6) _____ (be promoted). They (7) _____ (make) me Team Leader.

Jane: Oh, good news. What does 'Team Leader' mean exactly?

Dick: It means that I (8) _____ (accept) management responsibilities. They (9) _____ (give) me a red badge to wear.

Jane: You (10) _____ (move) up in the world!

🌐 **26 Listen and check.**

5 Underline the correct verb form.

One and a half billion dollars' worth of popcorn (1) **eat / <u>is eaten</u>** in the United States every year. In other words, every man, woman and child (2) **eats / is eaten** about one kilo per year. Sold in huge containers at the cinema, popcorn (3) **usually covers / is usually covered** with salt or sugar and (4) **washes down / washed down** with a fizzy drink. In many countries, coconut oil (5) **uses / is used** to cook the corn, which (6) **means / is meant** that an average portion of cinema popcorn (7) **contains / is contained** more fat than the body (8) **needs / is needed** in a single day.

6 Put the verbs in brackets in the correct form.

Popcorn (1) _____became_____ (become) popular in the 1920s, when food prices (2) _____ (rise) during the Great Depression. It was cheap and (3) _____ (make) easily in large quantities after the invention of the first electric popcorn machines. However, the art of making popcorn (4) _____ (discover) by Native Americans thousands of years ago. Christopher Columbus (5) _____ (greet) in the Caribbean by men wearing necklaces that (6) _____ (make) of popcorn. The corn (7) _____ (use) in religious ceremonies, but the Native Americans (8) _____ (also eat) it. Columbus (9) _____ (buy) a few of the necklaces to take home with him.

7 Rewrite the sentences beginning with the words given.

a) A friend is helping me with this exercise.

I _am being helped with this exercise by a friend._

b) My teacher will mark my homework.

My homework _____

_____

c) My sister is cooking my dinner this evening.

My dinner _____

_____

d) No one has ever given me a ring.

I _____

_____

e) No one will force me to take an English examination.

I _____

_____

f) I haven't opened my dictionary today.

My dictionary _____

_____

g) A friend invited me to their house last weekend.

I _____

_____

Change the sentences to make them true for you.

Pronunciation

1 ⊕ 27 **Listen to the words in the box. Is the underlined sound /s/ or /z/? Put the words in the correct column.**

~~always~~	~~a<u>s</u>k~~	belief<u>s</u>	chee<u>s</u>e	de<u>ss</u>ert
exten<u>s</u>ive	fu<u>ss</u>y	invi<u>s</u>ible	loo<u>s</u>e	noi<u>s</u>y
plea<u>s</u>e	re<u>s</u>taurant	the<u>s</u>e	thi<u>s</u>	

/s/	/z/
ask	always

⊕ 28 **Listen and check. Repeat the words.**

2 ⊕ 29 **Listen to the recording and practise saying the following groups of words.**

a) /sp/ spinach   spoonful   spread   sports   spill

b) /sk/ skipped   squeeze   scale   score   screen

c) /st/ steak   stick   stodgy   strict   stroke

Vocabulary

1 **Match the sentence beginnings (*a–f*) with their endings (1–6).**

a) He raised
b) He held
c) He stuck
d) She bent
e) She clenched
f) She shook

1 her finger to warn me of the danger.
2 her knees to speak to the small children.
3 her teeth to fight against the pain.
4 his arms to protect himself.
5 his chest out to show his muscles.
6 his head up to show he wasn't afraid.

a	b	c	d	e	f
4					

2 **Complete the sentences with the verbs in the box in the correct form.**

bend clench hold ~~raise~~ shake stick

a) A few eyebrows were ____raised____ when the first model appeared in a new Dior creation.
b) She _____ her head and said 'no'.
c) Don't _____ your tongue out – it's rude.
d) The teacher _____ her hand up and waited for the class to be quiet.
e) Can you touch your feet without _____ your legs?
f) He _____ his fists and shouted in wild anger.

3 **Underline the correct words.**

Guy: I've found a restaurant for tonight. They do a decent (1) **set** / **square** menu, but you can also eat (2) **à la carte** / **plain** if you prefer.

Moll: Have they got a (3) **stodgy** / **vegetarian** menu? You know I don't eat meat.

Guy: Yes, they've got some rather interesting (4) **regional** / **unique** dishes. It's all (5) **bland** / **organic** food, actually. I think you'll like it. They have a lot of fish (6) **dishes** / **food** too.

Moll: Are you sure it's OK? Not like the place with (7) **mild** / **paper** plates you took me to last time?

Guy: No, this is a lot more up-market. Their website says they specialise in the 'subtle (8) **flavours** / **plates** of Lebanese cuisine'.

🔊 30 **Listen and check.**

4 **Complete the text with the words in the box.**

dishes extensive flavour fresh
light ~~menu~~ three-course

I often have dinner at a restaurant called 'L'Ane Vert', or 'The Green Donkey' as you would say in English. Their à la carte (1) ___menu___ has a lot of local (2) _____ , with things like rabbit in beer or mussels and chips, but you can also have something (3) _____ , like a salad. The food is (4) _____ and the service is friendly. While I'm looking at the (5) _____ menu, I usually order a glass of Kriek, with its unmistakable (6) _____ of cherries. The portions here are big, so you won't need to order a (7) _____ meal unless you're really hungry.

5 **Complete the text with the phrases in the box.**

As a result In other words Secondly
To sum up ~~The first and most obvious reason~~
What is more In fact

I don't understand why so many people still go to fast food restaurants. We should do all we can to avoid them. (1) *The first and most obvious reason* for this is that the food they serve has very little nutritional value. (2) _____ , in large quantities, it is positively bad for us. We are encouraged to buy mega-size portions of greasy fries and one-litre cups of sugary fizz.
(3) _____ , every country in the industrialised world is suffering increased problems with obesity and heart disease. (4) _____ , these so-called restaurants are selling this high-calorie, high-fat food to adolescents, who need a healthy diet.
(5) _____ , this junk 'food' is sold in polluting containers that cannot be recycled when they are covered in ketchup. (6) _____ , a regular diet of burgers and fries with cola, ketchup and ice cream destroys not only your health but also the planet. (7) _____ , I think that fast food places should be closed down as an environmental health danger.

6 Match the sentence beginnings (*a–g*) with their endings (*1–7*).

a) Children can be very fussy
b) Other people shunned him
c) She likes to do her bit
d) The bank notes were all soggy
e) The infected animals were all
f) There's no way that you can retain
g) We were crammed

1 into the bus like sardines.
2 when I found them in a wet pocket.
3 to save the planet.
4 the high moral ground.
5 slaughtered.
6 after his stroke.
7 about what they eat.

a	b	c	d	e	f	g
7						

7 Complete the text with the phrases in the box.

> although   consequently   even though
> furthermore   however   ~~so~~   to sum up

The restaurant *Chez Marcel* is very busy,
(1) _____so_____ we had to book our dinner
five weeks in advance. (2) _____ the
restaurant has three Michelin stars, we did not enjoy
our visit. The food was bland and the meat was
overcooked. (3) _____ , the service was
awful. We were given a table near the toilets
(4) _____ we had booked a table by the
window. The waiter ignored us for most of the meal.
(5) _____ , we decided not to leave a
tip. It was, (6) _____ , a truly horrible
experience. (7) _____ , we had an even
worse meal the following day.

8 🌐 **31 Listen to the recording. Underline the numbers that you hear.**

a) <u>1959</u> / 19.59
b) 999 / 0.999
c) 1/100ᵗʰ / 100
d) 23,302 / 23,032
e) 07.05.2009 / 75,209
f) 0.20446544 / 020 44 6544
g) 2.1 / 21ˢᵗ

9 Underline the correct alternative.

a) Ana Ivanović beat her young opponent
   six <u>love</u> / **nought**, six **love** / **nought**.
b) Arsenal beat Leeds United five **love** / **nil**.
c) My telephone number is **nil** / **oh** two, three
   double one, double six double six.
d) Norway became independent from Sweden in
   nineteen **oh** / **zero** five.
e) Four fifths is the same as **love** / **nought** point
   eight.
f) The coldest recorded temperature on earth is
   eighty nine degrees below **oh** / **zero**.

🌐 **32 Listen and check.**

10 Cross out four inappropriate collocations. The first has been done for you.

bland food   ~~dark customers~~
bright lighting   chilled menu
corked wine   the prawns are off
overcooked customers overdone steak
noisy customers   rude service
slow service   unhelpful wine

11 Complete the idioms with the food in the illustrations.

a) feel like a real _____lemon_____ : feel foolish
b) go red as a _____ : become very
   visibly embarrassed
c) as nice as _____ : very nice
d) spill the _____ : reveal a secret
e) pay _____ : not pay very much
f) a smart _____ : an intelligent person
g) a big _____ : an important person
h) _____ someone up: be very nice to
   someone
i) take something with a pinch of _____ :
   not take something very seriously

Listening

1 🔘 33 Cover the listening script opposite. Look at the three newspaper headlines and listen to the recording. Which newspaper story has the man been reading?

> ## Speed eater suffers heart attack

> # New rules for fast food

> ## *Chestnut wins Hamburger Olympics*

2 Listen again and answer the questions.

a) How old is Joey Chestnut?

b) How much did he win?

c) How long did it take Joey Chestnut to eat 93 hamburgers?

d) How many burgers did the second-placed competitor eat?

e) How many hotdogs has Chestnut eaten in ten minutes?

f) What kind of sandwiches does he hold world records for?

g) How many competitive eating competitions take place every year?

h) How many people watched Chestnut win the Championship?

3 Look at the listening script and find seven verbs and phrasal verbs that mean 'eat'.

a) w*olfed down*

b) s_____

c) g_____

d) s_____

e) p_____

f) t_____

g) s_____

Husband:	Hey, have you seen this?
Wife:	What?
Husband:	This story in the paper. About some guy in America who's eaten 93 hamburgers in eight minutes.
Wife:	No!
Husband:	It was the World Hamburger Eating Championships.
Wife:	You're kidding.
Husband:	No, seriously. Listen. 'Joey Chestnut, 24, from San José, California, has taken the $20,000 first prize in the World Hamburger Eating Championships for the second year running. Chestnut wolfed down 93 Krystal burgers in eight minutes, ten less than the world record he holds, but enough to see off his closest challenger, Pat 'Deep Dish' Bertoletti, who could manage to swallow only 85 in the time available.'
Wife:	Sounds like a competition you would have a chance of winning.
Husband:	It's amazing. This guy, Joey Chestnut, is ranked number 1 in the world by the International Federation of Competitive Eating.
Wife:	The what?
Husband:	The International Federation of Competitive Eating, and he's got a whole pile of world records. In ten minutes, he can get down 66 hot dogs, 59 peanut butter sandwiches or stuff himself with 47 toasted cheese sandwiches.
Wife:	He must be completely mad, pigging himself like that. Can you imagine what it's doing to his health?
Husband:	Yeah, just think of all that stuff in his ...
Wife:	Some people, I mean they'll do anything to get into the Guinness Book of Records, but tucking in to a ton of hotdogs ...
Husband:	It says here that there are hundreds of these competitions around the US every year. It's on prime time TV and everything ...
Wife:	No!
Husband:	'Ten thousand people watched the event in Chattanooga, Tennessee,' that's what it says. They do burgers and hot dogs, pizzas, horseshoe sandwiches – whatever they are, chicken wings, fried asparagus – that's a weird one – and there's even a ...
Wife:	Asparagus!?
Husband:	You know what? I think I'll go and see if I can find a clip or something about it on YouTube .
Wife:	Oh, not now. Dinner will be ready in a minute. I'm almost done.
Husband:	Oh, OK. Later then, maybe.
Wife:	No need. I can just watch you scoffing your dinner. As usual.

Writing

Writing a discursive essay
Arguments for and against
Text organisation

1 Read the essay below and underline two reasons *for* and two reasons *against* buying organic food.

To be organic or not to be organic?

In recent years, there has been an explosion of shops and restaurants selling organic food. They are growing at 20% a year and nearly 2% of all worldwide food sales are now organic.

There are many good reasons for buying organic food and the first is that it is better for the future of our planet. *We know* that pesticides and some animal feeds are poisoning the world we live in. *What is more*, organic food is almost certainly better for your health and the health of your children. The advantages of eating organic food, both for you and for the environment, are obvious.

There is, however, one major drawback to buying organic food. It is more expensive and more difficult to find. Many families are in favour of the idea in principle, but cannot afford it in practice. Another strong argument against buying organic food is that you can't always be sure that it's organic. Buying local food, that has not been flown across an ocean, may *be a better way of helping the planet* than buying organic pineapples from West Africa.

It is understandable to have reservations about organic food, although I think we should all buy it when we can. I know that *some people may disagree*. Personally, I like to have a choice.

2 Complete the sentences with the prepositions in the box.

about	against	for	of	of	to

a) There is one drawback _____ buying organic food.

b) The advantages _____ eating organic food are obvious.

c) There are many good reasons _____ buying organic food.

d) Many families are in favour _____ the idea.

e) One argument _____ buying organic food is that you can't be sure it's organic.

f) It's understandable to have reservations _____ organic food.

Read the essay again to check your answers.

3 Find phrases in italics in the essay to match the phrases below.

a) It isn't difficult to find reasons

b) not everybody would agree

c) It is well known

d) benefit us more

e) An additional reason is that

f) I can understand that some people

4 You are going to write an essay about the **advantages and disadvantages of commercial deals between schools and fast food companies.**

Decide if the sentences below are *for* fast food companies supplying meals to schools or *against* it.

a) Most schools are very short of money and deals with fast food brands make a lot of money for the school.

b) School books are too expensive and fast food companies offer good-quality, free teaching materials.

c) Schools are educational places – children should learn about health education.

d) If young people eat more fast food, they will develop more health problems.

e) Young people should not be encouraged to eat junk food.

5 Complete the essay below with three more paragraphs. Use your own ideas and the ideas in Exercise 4. Use the phrases in Exercises 2 and 3. You should write approximately 180 words.

Fast food in schools?

1 If you go to school in the US, there's a chance that you can order your lunch from Subway, Pizza Hut or McDonald's. Maybe you won a free thick-crust pizza for reaching your reading targets. You'll almost certainly buy your Coke from the vending machine in the school's entrance area.

2 *Reasons for making fast food available in schools*

3 *Reasons for banning fast food in schools*

4 *Personal opinion*

7 Escape

Grammar

1 Correct the mistakes in the following sentences. In each sentence, remove one word only. One of the sentences is correct.

a) The travel agent suggested ~~us~~ that we go to Shoreham-by-the-Sea for our next holiday.

b) He assured to us that we would have a wonderful time.

c) He explained us that it had won an award for its clean beaches.

d) He also mentioned us that it had a fantastic nightlife.

e) He convinced to us that it was this year's top destination.

f) Finally, he persuaded to us to book it by offering a discount.

g) The company confirmed us that there would be no price increases.

h) One week before departure, the company announced us that there was a 5% price increase.

i) They told us that it was because of a rise in airport taxes.

2 Complete the second sentence so that it has a similar meaning to the first.

a) 'I did too little, too late,' he said.
He admitted _doing_ too little too late.

b) 'Be very careful,' she told him.
She advised _____ _____ _____ very careful.

c) 'I will return soon,' he said to me.
He assured _____ _____ he would return soon.

d) 'It'll be easy!' he said.
He claimed _____ _____ would be easy.

e) 'Yes, I am married,' she said.
She confirmed _____ _____ _____ married.

f) 'Go on! Buy it!' he said to her, pointing at the car.
He tried to persuade _____ _____ buy the car.

g) 'Go. Now!' she said to them.
She encouraged _____ _____ leave quickly.

3 Complete the second sentence with between two and four words so that it means the same as the first sentence.

a) It wasn't necessary for me to travel far for my last holiday.
I didn't _____ _have to travel_ _____ far for my last holiday.

b) I was only allowed to take 10 kilos of baggage with me.
I _____ take 10 kilos of baggage with me.

c) It was necessary for us to book the holiday a long time in advance.
We _____ the holiday a long time in advance.

d) We couldn't pay by credit card.
We were _____ pay by credit card.

e) Fortunately, we were permitted to use my parents' car.
Fortunately, we _____ my parents' car.

f) We were not allowed to park the car outside our accommodation.
We _____ the car outside our accommodation.

g) It wasn't necessary for us to spend much money.
We _____ to spend much money.

4 Write the words in order to make sentences.

a) better have I known should
I should have known better.

b) have I shouldn't trusted you
_____

c) have I shouldn't that said
_____

d) have I I'm sorry, should told you
_____

e) ended have It like shouldn't that
_____

f) at have home I should stayed
_____

Have you ever said the sentences above? What were the circumstances?

5 Underline the correct alternative.

a) I like watching **a** / **–** travel documentaries on **a** / **–** TV.

b) I never go to **a** / **–** place without buying **a** / **–** guide book before I go.

c) I am almost never at **–** / **the** home at **–** / **the** weekend or in **–** / **the** holidays.

d) There are **a** / **–** lot of places that I plan to visit in **–** / **the** next six months.

e) As **a** / **the** child, I enjoyed travelling by **–** / **a** car.

f) I don't care about **–** / **the** weather when I'm visiting **a** / **–** foreign country.

g) Holidays are more important to me than **–** / **the** money.

Change the sentences to make them true for you.

6 Complete the story with *a, an, the* or **–** (no article).

Mrs Camilla Rust, of Seaford in (1) *the* south of (2) _____ England, was shocked one morning to discover that (3) _____ gnome had disappeared from (4) _____ garden at (5) _____ front of her house, although (6) _____ other four were untouched. Ten days later, she received (7) _____ letter. In (8) _____ envelope, there was (9) _____ photograph of (10) _____ missing gnome standing in (11) _____ middle of (12) _____ Colisseum in (13) _____ Rome. (14) _____ next day, (15) _____ second letter arrived with (16) _____ French stamp on it. This time, (17) _____ gnome was photographed on (18) _____ mountain in (19) _____ east of (20) _____ France. (21) _____ letters continued every day for (22) _____ month, with (23) _____ photographs of (24) _____ gnome in (25) _____ different parts of (26) _____ world. Then, (27) _____ letters stopped. One morning, (28) _____ week later, Mrs Rust found (29) _____ missing gnome in its usual place in (30) _____ garden.

7 Insert the articles in the box in the correct places in the film synopsis.

A̶	a	a	a	a	an	the	the	the

The Holiday

Starring

Cameron Diaz, Kate Winslet, Jude Law

Synopsis

A

British woman, Iris Simpkins, and American woman, Amanda Woods, are both at end of relationship. They decide to take two-week holiday and go to live in other person's home. They want to forget about men. In small English village, Amanda meets and falls in love with Iris's brother. Meanwhile, in sunny California, Iris meets musician and love is in air there, too.

8 Correct the mistakes in these sayings.

a) You can't measure the happiness.
You can't measure happiness.

b) There never was the good war or bad peace.
_____

c) Friendship is love with the intelligence.
_____

d) Men never remember, but the women never forget.
_____

e) The money is power.
_____

f) Nothing is certain in the life except the death and taxes.
_____

g) A time waits for no one.
_____

h) Proverbs rarely contain the wisdom.
_____

Do you agree with the sentences above?

Vocabulary

1 **Solve the anagrams and use these words to complete the sentences about the pictures.**

YESVURING   a)   s _urveying_____

BLIBNING   b)   n_____

WELTO   c)   t_____

HYDING   d)   d_____

UNRUBNS   e)   s_____

GADDPLIN   f)   p_____

PEDSA   g)   s_____

In picture B ...

1   two men are playing Frisbee, not
_____surveying_____ the scene.

2   the man sunbathing does not have bad
_____ like the man in picture A.

3   the woman is not _____ in the water.

4   the son is in a _____ , not on a Li-Lo.

5   the dog is _____ a biscuit, not a sandwich.

6   the man is lying on the sand, not on a
_____ .

7   there is no _____ near the bucket.

2 **Match the words in the box with the definitions.**

> advise   assure   claim   convince
> mention   persuade   reassure   ~~suggest~~

a)   offer an idea for someone to consider
_____suggest_____

b)   give your opinion to someone about the best thing to do _____

c)   tell someone that something will happen or that something is true, so that there is no doubt _____

d)   make someone feel less worried about something _____

e)   make someone believe that something is true _____

f)   make someone agree to do something by giving them good reasons _____

g)   say something in conversation without giving it much importance _____

h)   say that something is true, even if there is no proof _____

3 **Underline the correct word.**

a)   He _____ that Manchester United had won the cup in 1997, but nobody agreed.

advised   <u>claimed</u>   mentioned   reassured

b)   I can _____ you that we will do everything possible to make your stay comfortable.

assure   claim   confirm   explain

c)   She accused me of lying and I had to _____ that I was.

admit   advise   inform   mention

d)   If you don't return the money, we will have to _____ the police.

advise   confirm   inform   suggest

e)   It was easy to _____ her to come with us.

admit   announce   mention   persuade

f)   The rumours were _____ when the photos were published in the newspapers.

assured   confirmed   convinced   encouraged

g)   You'll never _____ me that she was innocent.

claim   convince   insist   suggest

h)   Why do you _____ on speaking English all the time?

assure   confirm   encourage   insist

4 Tick the words which can be made into an adjective by adding the suffix *-ish*.

a) bull ✓   f) hell

b) child   g) humour

c) devil   h) pain

d) fool   i) self

e) help   j) taste

5 Make adjectives by adding *-ful* or *-less* to the words in the box and use these words to complete the sentences.

care	child	doubt	~~end~~
help	relent	stress	taste

a) There was an ___endless___ line of people waiting to receive food.

b) Be _____ with that – it's a dangerous weapon!

c) The British police have a reputation for being _____ to foreign visitors.

d) The food they serve is cold and _____ .

e) The noise of the neighbours' arguments is _____ – they never stop.

f) It's very _____ that you'll finish on time – you've hardly started.

g) It was a _____ marriage, but they were very happy together.

h) Some people say teaching is a _____ job, but they should try driving an ambulance.

6 Complete the sentences with the negative form of the adjectives in the box.

divided	~~legal~~	literate	logical
mature	polite	willing	

a) Drugs like marijuana are ___illegal___ in most countries.

b) To hide the fact that he was _____ , he said that he didn't like reading.

c) He was more than _____ – he was extremely rude.

d) She's still very _____ but she'll grow up soon.

e) Unfortunately, the bank was _____ to help me.

f) You may think that my decision is _____ but I can explain my reasons.

g) I would like your _____ attention, please.

7 Insert the missing letters.

When you arrive in Bruges, you (1) s*h o u l d* go to the main square, Markt, and go into the tallest building on the square, the Bell Tower. It's (2) w_ _ _ worth the effort to climb the 350 steps to the top for spectacular (3) v_ _ _ _ over the rooftops and canals of the town. After that, I'd definitely (4) r_ _ _ _ _ _ _ _ a canal trip. The experience can be a bit touristy, but you (5) w_ _ _ be disappointed if you choose the right time. It's probably best to (6) a_ _ _ _ the town altogether at busy weekends. In fact, if I (7) w_ _ _ you, I'd go in March when it's very quiet. (8) W_ _ _ _ _ _ _ you do, don't miss the 'Begijnhof' – it used to be a home for religious women – which is beautiful in the early spring. Another (9) m_ _ _ is the Memling museum, which is in a twelfth-century building. Oh, and make (10) s_ _ _ you buy some chocolate before you leave – the streets behind the Markt are the best (11) p_ _ _ _ _ to find chocolate shops.

🌐 **34 Listen and check.**

Pronunciation

🌐 **35 Listen to the way the expressions in italics are pronounced. Notice the way the voice goes up on the stressed syllable, which is underlined. Practise saying these expressions after the recording.**

a) *Actually*, it wasn't the best holiday we've had.

b) *To be honest*, we were a bit disappointed.

c) *Basically*, we should have done more research before we left.

d) *In fact*, we left it very late before making the booking.

e) *Anyway*, we tried to make the most of it.

f) *Come to think of it*, there were one or two moments that weren't too bad.

g) *In the end*, I think the children quite enjoyed themselves.

Reading

1 Read the article and answer the questions.

a) Was the article published in a magazine for men or for women? _____

b) Is the point of the article to give advice or to entertain? _____

2 Read the article again and insert the phrases (*a–g*) in the spaces (*1–7*) in the article.

a) and there are precious few shops above the snow line

b) preferably carrying something cold and beer-shaped

c) so it's worth looking

d) so that it won't be on the agenda later

e) so you never know quite where they are looking

f) where old passions are reunited in the heady fragrance of fine wines and tropical bougainvilleas

g) which is the last thing on earth you want to share a two-man tent with

3 Find the words and expressions in the text and choose the best definition.

a) *make themselves scarce*
   1 are frightened
   2 go away

b) *re-materialise*
   1 come back
   2 pay for everything

c) *tougher*
   1 more difficult
   2 stronger

d) *sulk*
   1 showing that you're happy
   2 showing that you're unhappy

e) *rotisserie*
   1 a piece of equipment for cooking meat
   2 a surfboard

f) *lingering*
   1 lasting for a long time
   2 lasting for a short time

g) *craft shops*
   1 shops selling clothes and shoes
   2 shops selling locally or traditionally produced objects

What men really want from a holiday

by GUY BROWNING

What men want on holiday is not much different to what men want at all times: the company of attractive women who make themselves scarce when there are toys to play with; and when they're bored with their toys they want the attractive women to re-materialise, (1) ____ . While men are playing, it's important that women use the time to get any shopping out of the way, (2) ____ .

Men like skiing because you get a lot of exercise, you can do it without holding hands all day (3) ____ . Men also like activity holidays with rafting, hiking, diving, etc. But try to remember that men are tougher than women and don't want you doing anything harder or more dangerous than they do. If you do, there'll be the world's largest sulk, (4) ____ .

Men like the idea of beach holidays because when you say the word 'beach' they hear 'bikini'. When men are in a bikini-rich environment they tend to keep their sunglasses on (5) ____ . Men also like a bit of sun, but they don't want to spend all week on the rotisserie. They'd rather do something energetic during which they get badly burnt.

Women want lingering, candlelit dinners under the stars, (6) ____ . Men require candle-light to identify the local variant of steak and chips on the menu. Remember, when men get that dreamy, faraway look in their eyes, it's generally because they've spotted football on the satellite television behind the bar.

Women like craft shops on holiday. Men don't like craft, they don't like shops and they certainly don't want to spend valuable leisure time going around foreign craft shops. Men know before they enter a craft shop that there is nothing inside that they could possibly ever want. Women know that there just might be something, (7) ____ . Men will come with you inside the shop, but they'll stand near the door watching other women pick up marble ashtrays.

Writing

Writing a description of a place
Sentence frames

1 Read the short article below and tick (✓) the topics which are mentioned.

a) cost   g) language
b) entertainment   h) local customs
c) famous inhabitants   i) museums
d) festivals   j) scenery
e) history   k) shopping
f) sports facilities   l) theatres

Sheffield

With a population of over half a million, Sheffield is England's fourth biggest city, but it remains unknown to many visitors to the country. The city suffered enormously in the 1980s, but there is more to this city than closed steel factories and abandoned coal mines. Although you may never have considered it as a tourist destination, it is worth taking a closer look.

Incredible as it may seem, Sheffield (in the middle of England) boasts one of Europe's largest all year round skiing complexes. (1) If that doesn't take your fancy, then an excursion out of town is a must. The city is surrounded by some of England's most beautiful countryside in the Peak District National Park. (2) But what really makes Sheffield stand out is its nightlife. This is a happening town – cinemas, restaurants, clubs and café-bars. (3) And all at half of the cost they would be in London.

a village in the Peak District

For overseas visitors, Sheffield deserves to be high on their list of places to visit. (4) Forget London, Oxford, Stratford and other tourist traps where you will be seeing a plastic, packaged and sanitized version of Ye Olde England. Sheffield is the real thing. (5) By the way, the accents are not too difficult, either.

---

2 Find the places (1–5) in the text where the following phrases should go.

a) Although you can still get your warm beer and milky tea, you're more likely to find people drinking cappuccino and Belgian beer. ☐

b) For those coming to learn the language, you can be sure of a warm welcome here. ☐

c) This is England as it really is – not the theme park version that most people see. ☐

d) True, it's an artificial slope, but who wants it to snow all year anyway? ☐

e) Wild moorlands, waterfalls and rocky peaks are just a stone's throw away. ☐

3 Complete the following sentences so that they are true for your town or area.

a) There is more to _____
than _____
_____

b) _____
_____
is particularly worth seeing.

c) _____
boasts one of the most _____
_____

d) If that doesn't take your fancy, then _____
_____
is a must.

e) What really makes _____
special is _____
_____

f) If you do visit _____ ,
it's a good idea to _____
_____

4 Imagine you work for the tourist office. Write a short report (approximately 180 words) for visitors to your town or area.

- Look at Exercise 1 and decide which topics you will include.

- Decide the order in which you will deal with these topics.

- Choose one aspect of your town/area to concentrate on for your final paragraph.

8 Attraction

Grammar

1 **Report the statements using the verb in brackets and a passive reporting structure.**

a) They have had an argument. (think)

It is thought that they have had an argument.

b) They are getting divorced. (say)

It _____

_____

c) An announcement will be made tomorrow. (believe)

It _____

_____

d) Frances has taken the children to the South of Spain. (suggest)

It has _____

_____

e) William wants custody of the children. (say)

It has _____

_____

f) Frances has fallen in love with a younger man. (believe)

It _____

_____

g) They will be getting married in the spring. (think)

It _____

_____

2 **Report the sentences using the words given.**

a) It is thought that chocolate relieves stress.

Chocolate *is thought to relieve stress.*

b) It is believed that blondes have more fun.

Blondes _____

c) It is thought that grey hair is attractive in men.

Grey hair _____

d) It was said that pale skin was a sign of great beauty.

Pale skin _____

e) It was once considered that cosmetic surgery was an expensive luxury.

Cosmetic surgery _____

_____

f) It is believed that brown eyes are stronger than blue eyes.

Brown eyes _____

_____

g) It is known that working in front of a computer screen is bad for your eyes.

Working in front of a computer screen _____

3 **Put the words in the correct order.**

a) examined eyes your Get!

Get your eyes examined!

b) having her is painted portrait She

_____

c) a had key made spare We

_____

d) car I get must the washed

_____

e) printed photos had Have your yet you ?

_____

_____

f) cleaned had It's the time we windows

_____

_____

g) bags Could have my room sent my to up you ?

_____

_____

4 Complete the second sentence in each pair so that it means the same as the first sentence.

a) I went for an eye test last week.
I had *my eyes tested* last week.

b) Why don't you take your shoes to the repair shop?
Why _____ get your shoes _____ ?

c) Your hair is far too long.
You should get _____ .

d) We're going to ask the builder to knock down this wall.
We're _____ have _____ down.

e) The company have decided to change their logo.
The company are _____ get their logo _____ .

f) The garage checked the car last week.
We had _____ last week.

g) I want to have an operation to straighten my nose.
I _____ get my _____ .

h) Someone should check your homework.
You _____ get your _____ .

5 Write questions using the prompts.

a) How often / you get / hair / cut?
How often do you get your hair cut ⎯

b) you ever / consider / have / tattoo /do ?
_____
_____

c) When / last time / you have / eyes /test ?
_____
_____

d) Where /you usually get / photos / print ?
_____
_____

e) you ever / think about / get / name / change ?
_____
_____

f) How often / you have / nails / manicure ?
_____
_____

g) Where / usually go / get / shoes / repair ?
_____
_____

h) When / last time / you get / key / cut ?
_____
_____

Write true answers to the questions.

6 Use the words in brackets to make correct sentences. Make any other changes that are necessary.

a) If you find some money on the street, what would you do with it? (were to)
If you were to find some money on the street, what would you do with it?

b) Would you have cosmetic surgery, you had the money to pay for it? (assuming)
_____
_____

c) You could make a radical change to your lifestyle, what change would you make? (imagine)
_____
_____

d) Suppose someone give you three wishes, what would you wish for? (were to)
_____
_____

e) Who would you choose you were to get the chance to spend an evening with the celebrity of your choice? (supposing)
_____
_____

f) What job would you like to do, money, time and talent were no object? (assuming)
_____
_____

Write true answers to the questions.

Pronunciation

1 🔘 36 Look at the phrases below and listen to the recording. Notice how the stress changes.
He's very warm-<u>heart</u>ed.
He's a <u>warm</u>-hearted person.

2 🔘 37 Listen and underline the stressed syllable in the following compound adjectives.
a) absent-minded
b) big-headed
c) easy-going
d) good-looking
e) level-headed
f) open-minded
g) self-centred
h) laid-back

Vocabulary

1 Label the picture using the words in the box.

| cheekbone | dimple | ~~eye~~ | eyebrow | jaw |

a) _eye_   b) _____   c) _____

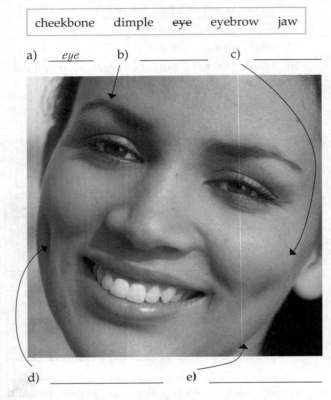

d) _____   e) _____

2 Underline one noun in each group that can be described by the adjective in bold.

a) **smooth**   eyes, nose, <u>skin</u>
b) **white**   lips, teeth, smile
c) **sparkling**   bone structure, eyes, dimples
d) **square**   cheekbones, jaw, nose,
e) **big**   bone structure, skin, smile
f) **turned-up**   eyes, cheekbones, nose
g) **high**   cheekbones, eyebrows, lips
h) **arched**   dimples, eyebrows, teeth
i) **full**   lips, skin, teeth

3 Which expressions in Exercise 2 *cannot* be used to describe the face in the photo.

4 Complete the description of the woman in the photo using words from Exercises 1 and 2. Use one word in each gap.

She has a classically beautiful face. She has a beautiful, (1) _big_ smile and wonderful, perfectly (2) _____ teeth. Her lips are (3) _____ and her skin is (4) _____ and clear. She has very good (5) _____ structure, with (6) _____ cheekbones and a pretty, heart-shaped face. She has (7) _____ in her cheeks which add to the youthfulness of her expression, as do the softly arched (8) _____ and her bright, sparkling (9) _____ .

5 Match the two halves of the adjectives.

a) self-   back
b) grown-   centred
c) laid-   headed
d) level-   minded
e) open-   to-earth
f) down-   up

6 Match the adjectives in Exercise 5 with the definitions below.

1 _____ _self-centred_ _____ : too interested in yourself so you don't think about what other people feel or need

2 _____ : calm and easy-going, not worried about problems and not easily stressed

3 _____ : behaving in a calm and rational way, even in a difficult situation

4 _____ : willing to consider new ideas, not having prejudices

5 _____ : practical and realistic, doesn't panic or react emotionally

6 _____ : looking or acting like a responsible adult

7 Complete the texts using the adjectives in Exercise 6.

a) She's so _____ _self-centred_ _____ . It's always 'me, me, me' and she never listens to a word anyone else says.

b) You know, I really don't think Donna is very _____ at all. She's always judging people and finding fault in everything they do.

c) That wasn't very _____ , was it? Do you think that putting glue on my seat is funny? I wish you'd act your age!

d) He's so famous and so successful, but when you get talking to him, you realise he's really simple, ordinary and totally _____ .

e) Jake is just so _____ . He's great, he never, ever panics and always knows what to do in an emergency.

f) He's so _____ he's half asleep! Nothing ever seems to stress him out .

8 Replace the adjectives in Exercise 7 with the adjectives in the box.

mature   relaxed   ~~selfish~~   sensible
tolerant   unpretentious

a) _selfish_   d) _____
b) _____   e) _____
c) _____   f) _____

9 Insert the missing vowels to complete the adjectives in the descriptions below.

Cancer
You are (1) s_e_ns_i_t_i_v_e and (2) c_r_ng. You are a very good friend and a passionate lover.

Leo
You are (3) s_ns_bl_ , (4) pr_ct_c_l and totally (5) tr_stw_rthy. You tend to be very (6) c_nv_nt__n_l in your opinions.

Virgo
You are (7) _n_gm_t_c and some people think you are (8) _nfr_ _ndly, but you are incredibly loyal and always totally (9) d_p_nd_bl_ .

10 Underline the correct adjective. In three of the sentences both adjectives are correct.

a) Jenny's really **caring** / **selfish**. She'd make a great nurse.

b) Tom is just so cold and **stand-offish** / **unfriendly**. He never says hello and just walks away when I try to start a conversation!

c) I think we need someone quite **experienced** / **mature** for the job of project manager.

d) One of the most important things for me in a relationship is trust. I need my partner to be totally honest and **trustworthy** / **dependable**.

e) There's something very **level-headed** / **mysterious** about the way she behaves. It's as if she has something to hide.

f) Her parents are so **straight** / **open-minded**. They just don't know how to react to their daughter's strange choice of friends.

11 Underline the correct word in these idioms.

a) put my **foot** / **mouth** in it
b) play it by **ear** / **nose**
c) a **chest** / **shoulder** to cry on
d) get it off my **chest** / **head**
e) up to my **ears** / **eyes** in work
f) be from this **leg** / **neck** of the woods
g) made my **head** / **mind** up
h) have his **feet** / **fingers** in a lot of pies

12 Match the idioms in Exercise 11 with the situations below.

1 I can't come out tonight, I've got two reports to finish. [e]

2 I asked Ben if he was looking forward to the party. Of course, he knew nothing about it and I completely ruined the surprise. [ ]

3 She's a local artist. She was born and brought up here. [ ]

4 I really didn't know what to do, so I made a list of advantages and disadvantages and that helped me come to my final decision. [ ]

5 I don't think we need to decide all the details right now. We can make those kinds of decision when we get there. [ ]

6 I was really annoyed with my boss, so I went for a drink with Beth and told her all about it. [ ]

7 Sally's a really good friend. She's always there for you when things go wrong and she's a great listener. [ ]

8 He works as an accountant during the day, he runs a small restaurant in the evenings and at the weekends he DJs at our local club. [ ]

13 Replace the phrases in bold with one of the idioms in Exercise 11.

a) Oh, sorry, **did I say something wrong**?
   did I put my foot in it?

b) I really need to **tell someone what happened**.
   _____

c) He finally **came to a decision**.
   _____

d) They **don't live near here**.
   _____

e) I just need **someone to show me their sympathy**.
   _____

f) **I've got loads of stuff to get done** today.
   _____

g) Let's **not make any specific plans**.
   _____

h) They **are working on a lot of different projects**.
   _____

Listening

1 🌐 **38 Listen to Lara and Jake on a speed date. Tick the topics they talk about.**

hobbies ✓
family __
friends __
tattoos __
jewellery __
travel __

2 **Listen again and decide if the statements are true (*T*) or false (*F*).**

a) Jake collects stamps. __
b) Lara's father collects stamps. __
c) Jake's father is a postman. __
d) Jake has a tattoo. __
e) Lara hasn't had her ears pierced. __
f) Lara doesn't like tattoos. __
g) Lara has a tattoo. __
h) Jake wants another date with Lara. __

3 **Listen again or read the script and find expressions that mean:**

a) I'm joking
    1 _____
    2 _____

b) You're joking, aren't you?
   _____

c) I'm sure
   _____

d) The same thing is true about …
   _____

e) Wait a minute
   _____

f) There's no time left
   _____

Lara: Hi, Jake.

Jake: Hello there, Lara.

Lara: So, Jake, tell me one interesting thing about yourself.

Jake: Interesting? Well, I collect stamps. I've been collecting stamps since I was about seven.

Lara: Stamps?

Jake: No, I'm only kidding ... do I look like a stamp collector? I mean, you know, stamps are about the most boring thing on earth.

Lara: Actually, my dad's a philatelist.

Jake: A philate – what?

Lara: A philatelist – he studies stamps, he works for the British Museum.

Jake: Oh, sorry, I just put my foot in it, didn't I? I mean, you know ...

Lara: Nah, I'm just pulling your leg – he's a postman actually.

Jake: Postman? Ha, ha – good one.

Lara: So, anyway, you still haven't told me anything interesting ...

Jake: OK ... well, I've got a tattoo of a Chinese lion in a very interesting place ...

Lara: Oh yes? And where would that be?

Jake: Sorry, can't tell you, you'll have to get to know me a bit better first ... Hey, *you* should have a tattoo done.

Lara: Yeah, what kind of tattoo?

Jake: I don't know. A flower maybe, or a bird ... I can't really make up my mind.

Lara: Yeah, well, the thing is, I don't really agree with tattoos – you know, I don't think we should mess around with our bodies like that ... and what about when you get older? I mean, will you still want a Chinese lion when you're in your 70s? The same goes for piercings .... I mean, they're OK when you're young ... but when you get older ...?

Jake: What, not even your ears? Come on, I bet you've had your ears pierced ... everybody's had their ears pierced ... Hey, hold on, you're having me on again, aren't you? Let's see your ears? Pierced?

Lara: Yes. You were a bit slow there, weren't you?

Jake: Yeah, OK ... OK .... don't you take anything seriously?

Lara: I try not to.

Jake: You know, you've got very pretty ears – and I love your earrings.

Lara: Thank you ...

Jake: Are you sure you haven't got a tattoo?

Lara: Well, yes, I have actually. Look. Here ...

Jake: Oh, wow, that's really great .... It's so small, I hadn't noticed it. Let me have a closer look ... Oh no, time's up. Can I see you again? I promise not to talk about stamps.

Writing

Writing a description of a person
Planning your writing

1 Scan the description below quickly and decide which actor it is about. (Some phrases are missing.)

George Clooney   *Will Smith*

● He's not classically good-looking. He doesn't have the macho appeal of Denzel Washington or the bone structure of Orlando Bloom. He's not cute like Johnny Depp or handsomely tough like Brad Pitt. But he certainly has that certain something which is often called the 'It' factor. What is it about this man that makes so many of us regularly go to see his movies?

● (1) are the eyes. With bushy eyebrows and heavy lids, he has the sort of warm brown eyes (2) he is the sensitive sort. With his kind, gentle and caring expression, (3) understand you. He would know what to say to cheer you up when you are feeling down.

● (4) his strong masculine chin. This, and his usual unshaved look, contrast with the sensitivity of his eyes. It is this mixture of strength and softness (5) attractive. (6), his other features are unexceptional. His hair is short and greying. His nose is straight and, well, normal. He just seems like a regular guy.

● He seems to prefer casual clothes, which go well with his five o'clock shadow. A white T-shirt and jacket perhaps, nothing too formal, but he still looks smart and respectable. In fact, (7) man you could introduce to your mother. She is probably a fan, too!

2 Find the places (1–7) in the text where the following phrases should go.

a) Another striking feature is ☐
b) Apart from that ☐
c) he looks like the sort of ☐
d) that makes him so ☐
e) The first thing you notice about him ☐
f) he looks as if he would ☐
g) that make you think ☐

3 Rearrange the words below to make the beginnings of sentences.

a) He just like looks
   He looks just like _____

a) from he Judging looks the way
   _____

b) about him is me most strikes What
   _____

c) about him is something that There
   _____

d) a He like looks typical
   _____

e) appears At glance first he to
   _____

f) an gives He impression of being
   _____

4 Describe a person you know and show how the way they look reveals their personality. The notes below may help you.

• Choose someone to describe. It may help to have a photograph of them in front of you. It doesn't matter if you don't know about their personality. You can make guesses based on their appearance.

• Brainstorm two short lists of adjectives and other phrases: one to describe their appearance; one to describe their personality.

• Decide what is most noticeable about their face or their clothes. What does this tell you about them?

• If you know the person well (or you have seen them on TV), how do they stand, walk, use their hands, move? What facial expressions do they often have? What does this tell you about their personality?

• How do you feel about this person? You may like to close your description with your personal view.

You can write in a formal or an informal way, but be consistent. You should write approximately 180 words.

9 Genius

Grammar

1 Underline the correct verb in the mini conversations.

a) A: Do you know where my iPod is?

   B: Yes, it's in the bathroom. You **must** / **can't** have left it there this morning.

b) A: I've finished.

   B: You **can't** / **might** have finished already!

c) A: Did I tell you about my friend Roger?

   B: I think you **can't** / **might** have told me, but I've forgotten. Tell me again.

d) A: I can't stop thinking about where he might be.

   B: Yes, anything **could** / **must** have happened to him!

e) A: My ex-boyfriend starred in a film once.

   B: Really? With looks like his, it **may** / **must** have been *Planet of the Apes*.

f) A: I'm sorry, but I think I **can't** / **may** have been a little impolite to you yesterday.

   B: Impolite? I thought you were quite rude, actually.

2 Think about the president or leader of your country and write five sentences about what he or she probably did yesterday. You can use the ideas in the box to help you.

> Good or bad day?   Meetings?
> Time up in the morning?   Lunch and dinner?
> Entertainment in the evening?   Time to bed?

a) He/She may have _____

_____

b) He/She might have _____

_____

c) He/She could have _____

_____

d) He/She must have _____

_____

e) He/She can't have _____

_____

3 Find and correct eight mistakes in the texts. The first one has been done for you.

> Some people think that the CIA may have ~~kill~~ *killed* President Kennedy. They say that Lee Harvey Oswald can't been responsible for the shooting and the CIA may be have murdered him in prison as a way of stopping the investigation.

> A survey in the US found that one in five people think that the Apollo astronauts must never have landed on the moon. They think that the film of the event must have being done with trick photography. Some people even believe that the government might have faked all the Apollo missions.

> It has been suggested by some people that the US government could has made secret contact with aliens. A mysterious crash at the Roswell military airport in 1947 may have be an alien spacecraft. Since then, it is thought that the government may kept another 11 similar incidents secret.

Tick the theories which you think might be true.

4 Rewrite the sentences using the modal verb given.

a) Perhaps I made a mistake.
   (may)
   I *may have made a mistake.*

b) I'm sure you were very surprised.
   (must)
   You _____

c) I think it's possible that I've seen this film before.
   (might)
   I _____

d) I'm almost certain she didn't tell the truth.
   (can't)
   She _____

e) I'm uncertain whether I paid or not.
   (may)
   I _____

f) There's a possibility that he's already left.
   (could)
   He _____

5 Complete the sentences about the picture below with *as if / as though*, *like* or – (if no word is needed).

a) It looks _____ – _____ terribly complicated.

b) It looks _____ a machine for peeling potatoes.

c) It doesn't look _____ very practical.

d) It looks _____ the machine is very slow.

e) It looks _____ the man has been repairing it.

f) It doesn't look _____ something that many people would want to buy.

g) The man looks _____ very old.

h) He looks _____ a mad professor.

6 Correct the mistakes. Tick (✓) the two sentences that are correct.

a) That seems like a very good idea. ✓

_____

b) He appears to being asleep.

_____

c) It seems if we've been here before.

_____

d) They are look like rain clouds.

_____

e) The local people all seemed like very friendly.

_____

f) I seem to get poorer and poorer every year.

_____

g) The club looked as if cool, so we went in.

_____

h) You look as you've seen a ghost.

_____

7 Write the words in order to make sentences.

a) as looks It it'll rain though today
   It looks as though it'll rain today.

b) angry bright is he he looks red When

_____

c) all classmates friendly My seem very

_____

d) a I little look mornings often on Saturday tired

_____
_____

e) a as has hit if it kitchen looks My tornado

_____
_____

f) appear be calm I I'm not often to when

_____
_____

g) a famous film I like look People say star that

_____

h) as English fast if improving is It my seems very

_____
_____

Change the sentences to make them true for you.

Pronunciation

🔘 **39** You will hear these sentences twice, but they will be said differently. Each time you hear a sentence, decide if (i) or (ii) is the most probable continuation.

a) She may have forgotten. ☐ ☐
   i) But I wouldn't have thought so.
   ii) She often does.

b) I might have left them at home. ☐ ☐
   i) I'll get them later.
   ii) Or they may be in the car.

c) It may have been an accident. ☐ ☐
   i) But it didn't look like one.
   ii) He wouldn't do it on purpose.

d) It could have been the wind, I suppose. ☐ ☐
   i) It was really strong last night.
   ii) But it looks more like a car drove into it.

e) He might have finished by now. ☐ ☐
   (i) I'll give him a ring to see.
   (ii) But it usually takes much longer.

Listen to the recording again and practise saying the sentences in the two different ways.

Vocabulary

1 Complete the sentences with the words in the box.

contemporary	derelict	eccentric	tough
hideous	run-down	~~shiny~~	sprawling

a) He liked to keep his car looking bright and
_____shiny_____ .

b) The shopping centre is a little _____
but they're planning to redevelop it soon.

c) Charles prefers traditional architecture and
hates most _____ buildings.

d) She was brought up in a _____ part
of the city, where there was a lot of crime.

e) She looked very _____ , with her
wild black hair and strange clothes.

f) The town was absolutely _____ ,
with not a single attractive building.

g) The squatters lived in a _____ house,
surrounded by other abandoned properties.

h) The _____ suburbs stretched as far as
the eye could see.

2 Match the definitions below to words in Exercise 1.

a) built over a wide area in a way that is ugly or
not carefully planned _____sprawling_____

b) very ugly _____

c) empty, unused and in bad condition
_____

d) in bad condition because money has not been
spent on repairs _____

e) modern _____

f) strange and unusual _____

3 Underline the correct alternative.

a) The 'Wall of Death' is the **captivating** / **main**
draw at my local theme park.

b) It was **drizzling** / **intriguing** outside, but I
hadn't brought my umbrella.

c) They **endured** / **existed** six years of prison
before they were set free.

d) There isn't much **spitting** / **incentive** for some
people to find a job.

e) He looked **overcast** / **enigmatic**, but very little
was happening in his head.

f) She was a **mere** / **mysterious** twelve years old
when she wrote her first novel.

4 Complete the text with the words in the box.

after	at	During	From	Just	On
Over	soon	~~When~~	while		

(1) ___When___ Felix Lope
de Vega y Carpio, usually
known as Lope de Vega,
was five, he could already
read Spanish and Latin.
He (2) _____ began
translating Latin poems
into Spanish and he wrote
his first play (3) _____
the age of twelve. (4) _____ then on, he almost
never put down his pen. (5) _____ the next fifty
years, he wrote more than a thousand plays and
hundreds of poems.

(6) _____ his youth, Lope spent some time
in the army and he had a short spell in prison.
(7) _____ his release from prison, he was
ordered to leave his home city of Madrid. He took
with him his sixteen-year old girlfriend and married
her. (8) _____ a few weeks after his wedding,
Lope de Vega left his wife and joined the army
again.

At the end of the war with England, he returned
to Spain, to his wife and to writing in Valencia.
However, (9) _____ the death of his wife, he was
able to return to Madrid, where he had a series of
relationships and married a second time. It was
(10) _____ he was in Madrid that he wrote his
best-known works. He died in 1635, an old man
of 72.

🔊 **40 Listen and check.**

**5 Match the sentence beginnings (a–f) with their
endings (1–6).**

a) Airbus developed
b) I've just come up with
c) More than 10,000 people apply for
d) The businessman set up
e) The policeman said he needed to conduct
f) The professor carried out

1 a brilliant idea to save the world.
2 a full body search.
3 a prototype of the A380 Superjumbo in 2005.
4 British patents every year.
5 experiments on his own students.
6 the company with his wife's money.

a	b	c	d	e	f
3					

6 Complete the texts using the prompts in brackets.

Before writing *The God Delusion*, Richard Dawkins was famous for his books about (1) __genetics__ (geneti-), such as *The Selfish Gene*. Both of his parents had an interest in (2) _____ (biolog-), and Dawkins studied zoology at university. After graduating, he worked as a research (3) _____ (scien-) on a project investigating how animals make decisions. Before retiring, he worked as a professor of (4) _____ (scien-) at the University of Oxford.

Cover from "Selfish Gene" by Richard Dawkins/by permission of Oxford University Press.

Steven Levitt, a Chicago (5) _____ (econom-), and Stephen Dubner, a New York journalist, wrote the multi-million best-seller *Freakonomics* in 2005. They apply (6) _____ (econom-) theory to a wide variety of odd subjects such as the Ku Klux Klan or the way that parents choose their children's names. You need a certain amount of (7) _____ (mathemat-) knowledge to understand the statistics, but this is a fun way to learn about (8) _____ (econom-).

Stephen Hawking is a theoretical (9) _____ (physic-) and applied (10) _____ (mathemat-) at the University of Cambridge. His book *A Brief History of Time* has sold nine million copies. Suffering from motor neurone disease, Hawking uses all the latest (11) _____ (technolog-) advances to communicate his ideas.

7 Read the instructions and number the arrows 1, 2 and 3. Insert the missing letters.

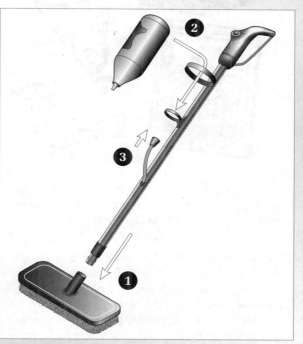

SWIFF-EEZE©
INSTRUCTIONS FOR USE

❶ In_s_e_rt the handle into the SWIFF-EEZE© brush. E_ _ur_ that the connection is secure by pushing until you hear it c_i_k.

❷ Pla_ e a SWIFF-EEZE© refill cartridge in the holder at the top of the handle. Turn c_o_k_i se.

❸ Connect the sp_ut of the refill cartridge to the plastic tube on the handle. To r_m_ _e an empty cartridge, p_e_s the button on the handle.

SWIFF-EEZE© **for easy swiffing**

8 One word in each sentence belongs to another sentence. Rewrite the sentences with the correct words.

a) He turned the tight on the thermostat to zero.

b) You can't turn it on until you've holder it in at the wall.

c) How did people change channels before they invented dial controls?

d) Make sure the lid's on place before you switch it on.

e) Put a cup under the plugged where the water comes out and push the blue button, OK?

f) Take the filter out of the remote and replace it after every cup of coffee that you make.

Reading

1 Read the text to find the connection between the four pictures.

Leonardo da Vinci's works of art made him world-famous. But there was far more to this great man of ideas than just the *Mona Lisa*'s pretty face.

— **1** —

The notebooks are full of drawings and designs for all kinds of inventions – from calculating machines to tanks, from parachutes to helicopters. If we also consider his studies of the human body, it is not hard to see why Leonardo is thought to be one of the greatest geniuses of all time.

— **2** —

Leonardo was particularly fascinated by the technology of war. At this time, Florence was at war with the Pope, and Leonardo realised that this was an opportunity to make some serious money with his new inventions for better guns and other military equipment. However, the war ended before his machines could be built and he returned to his painting.

But Leonardo had had enough of life in Florence, and especially of the other intellectuals who were jealous of him. He began to feel that his life would be better somewhere else.

— **3** —

When Sforza was driven from power by the French, Leonardo returned to Florence and spent four years working for Cesare Borgia as an engineer and military architect. He now became fascinated with flight. He studied birds and drew pictures of machines that looked like helicopters.

— **4** —

He ended his life at Amboise in France, where he was welcomed by King François I. He continued to make occasional drawings, a few designs and plans for buildings, but he spent most of his time sorting out his scientific papers.

Only twenty-one of his dozens of notebooks survive. We can only be sure that Leonardo did seventeen paintings, and some of these are unfinished. Leonardo did not perhaps achieve the perfection that he dreamed of, but he came closer to it in more fields than anyone before or since.

2 Decide where the following paragraphs should go in the text about Leonardo.

— **a** ☐ —

At the age of thirty, he left his home town and eventually moved to Milan, where he spent seventeen years working for Ludovico Sforza, the Duke of Milan. Here he continued to combine his scientific and technological work with his painting, which was increasingly influenced by his interest in mathematics. During this period, he painted *The Last Supper* and developed his ideas for chemical weapons and flame-throwers.

— **b** ☐ —

Born in 1452 to a Florentine lawyer and a local village girl, Leonardo was given only a very basic education. After ten years in the workshop of the artist Verrocchio, he began to work for himself. Some of the work he did still survives, and it shows an incredible combination of technical skills and very careful observation. It also shows that he was becoming fascinated with technology, with technical drawings of equipment of all kinds.

— **c** ☐ —

In 1506 he returned to Milan and became increasingly interested in science. He began to study human bodies and the circulation of the blood. He also studied many other animals, comparing their bodies to the human body.

— **d** ☐ —

Leonardo is often thought of primarily as an artist, and with works like *The Last Supper* and the *Mona Lisa*, his place in art history is certain. But his notebooks, filled with his strange, spidery writing, show that his main interests were in engineering and technology.

🌐 **41 Listen and check.**

3 Read the text again and write questions for the following answers.

a) _____

Verrocchio's.

b) _____

With the Pope.

c) _____

Seventeen years.

d) _____

When he was working for Borgia.

e) _____

Sorting out his scientific papers.

f) _____

At least seventeen.

Writing

Writing a story
Narrative tenses
Use of pronouns
Lexical variety: nouns

1 **Read the text below and choose the best sentence to end the story.**

a) At a news conference later, Waters said that he had done it because 'you can't just sit around'.

b) It was a helicopter belonging to the US Air Force.

c) He had liked balloons since he was a child.

> California truck driver, Larry Waters, was always wanting to be a pilot. The only way open for *him* to do *this* was to join the US Air Force, but poor eyesight made *this* impossible. He didn't give up and began work on the plan for his first flight.
>
> He bought 45 weather balloons from a local store and had filled *them* with helium gas. He fixed *these* to his garden chair, *which* was in turn tied to his jeep. For this epic journey, he also purchased some beer, a parachute and a two-way radio. When everything was ready, he got into the seat and cut the ropes attaching *it* to the jeep.
>
> His scheme worked well, at least at first. But the balloons continued to lift him up until he had reached the altitude of 5000 metres. Fortunately he had bought an air-gun which he could use to burst the balloons. He managed to burst ten of them, but then, unfortunately, he dropped the pistol. By now, he panicked.
>
> Waters' flying garden chair began to get dangerously close to Los Angeles International Airport. Jet pilots who were flying nearby were astonished to see the bizarre sight, but this was a potentially dangerous situation. An airport helicopter had eventually succeeded in bringing him back to earth.

2 **In each paragraph, there is one mistake with a narrative tense. Correct the mistakes.**

3 **In order to make a text more interesting, it is a good idea to avoid repeating words. Find synonyms in the text that are used instead of the following words.**

a) scheme _____

b) flight _____

c) bought _____

d) chair _____

e) air-gun _____

4 **Look at the words in italics in the first two paragraphs. Who or what do they refer to?**

a) him   *Larry Walters* _____

b) this _____

c) this _____

d) them _____

e) these _____

f) which _____

g) it _____

5 **Read the story below and rewrite it, choosing an appropriate narrative tense for the verbs in brackets. Where necessary, change the words in italics, using pronouns or alternative vocabulary.**

At the end of his act, the Argentinian magician, Professor Marvo, (ask) a male member of the audience who (sit) near the front to come on stage. *Professor Marvo* (hand) *the member of the audience* a gun and (ask) *the member of the audience* to shoot *Professor Marvo* in the face. *The member of the audience* (fire) the gun and *Professor Marvo* then (pull) the bullet from between his teeth.

The member of the audience (be) so impressed that he (take) another gun out of his pocket. While Professor Marvo (prepare) to leave the stage, *the member of the audience* said to *Professor Marvo*, 'Catch this!' and (shoot) *Professor Marvo*. *Professor Marvo* was killed instantly. Even during the subsequent trial, *the member of the audience* could still not understand why Professor Marvo (fail) to catch the bullet.

6 **Write a short story which ends with the following sentence:**

It's hard to believe that anyone could have been so stupid.

Write about 180 words.

10 Sell

Grammar

1 Insert commas into these sentences where necessary.

a) The most expensive advert of all time, which was for the drink Guinness, cost $20 million.

b) It was made by Nicolai Fuglsig whose other adverts include the Sony Bravia advert.

c) It is thought to be one of the most effective adverts that has ever been made.

d) One of the advertising companies which has had the highest sales worldwide is Dentsu Inc.

e) Castlemaine XXXX which is a kind of beer once showed 17 different TV adverts on one channel in one evening.

f) An advert that was made for British Airways had over 6,000 people in it.

g) The longest advertising poster ever produced which was made by O'Canada Gear in Alberta was over 332m long.

h) Eight songs that came from Levi jeans ads have got to number 1 in the British hit parade.

i) Guy Ritchie who used to be Madonna's husband has directed a soccer advert for Nike.

j) Nike which is one of the best known brands worldwide spent more than $1.7 billion on advertising in one year.

2 Complete the advertising slogans with an appropriate relative pronoun.

a) the taste _that_ bites

b) for the girl _____ can't say no

c) the man _____ has everything

d) the perfume _____ they wanted to ban

e) at a price _____ you won't find anywhere else

f) a man _____ life has been devoted to one thing

g) the face _____ launched a thousand ships

h) an experience _____ you will never forget

i) for those _____ time is precious

In three of these slogans the relative pronoun can be omitted. Which ones?

3 Combine the two sentences to make one sentence with a relative clause.

a) *Quantum of Solace* was first released in the UK. *Quantum of Solace* is the 22nd Bond film.

   Quantum of Solace, which is the 22nd Bond film, was first released in the UK.

b) Lots of Bond fans enjoyed Daniel Craig's performance in *Casino Royale*. They are glad to see him back in the role of 007.

   _____

   _____

   _____

c) Olga Kurylenko plays the role of a Russian-Bolivian agent. She helps Bond in his search for revenge.

   _____

   _____

   _____

d) Mathieu Almaric plays the role of the villain. Bond must try to stop this villain.

   _____

   _____

   _____

e) The title for the film is based on a short story. The short story appeared in a collection called *For Your Eyes Only*.

   _____

   _____

   _____

f) The film is directed by Marc Forster. Marc Forster also directed the Oscar-winning *Monster's Ball*.

   _____

   _____

   _____

4 Rewrite the following story. Include the extra information that is given below by using relative clauses.

One day, Philip K Wrigley was sitting on a plane. During the flight, the man asked, 'Why do you continue to advertise a chewing gum?' Wrigley quickly replied, 'For the same reason that the pilot of this plane keeps the engine running.'

- Philip K Wrigley was the founder of the famous chewing gum company.
- The flight was going to Chicago.
- The man was sitting next to Philip K Wrigley.
- The chewing gum was already the most popular in the world.
- Philip K Wrigley was known for his wit.
- The plane was flying at 30,000 feet in the air.

One day, Philip K Wrigley, who was the founder
_____
_____
_____
_____
_____
_____
_____
_____
_____
_____
_____
_____
_____

5 Match the beginnings of the quotations (*a–f*) with their endings (*1–6*).

a) What I least like about being famous
b) There's only one thing I don't like about being famous
c) The most challenging job I've ever had
d) All I really want to do
e) One thing I hate about Hollywood
f) The hardest thing I've ever had to do

1 and that's not having time to do everything that people want me to do. (Ricky Martin)
2 is being a mother. (Michelle Pfeiffer)
3 is people assuming you're fascinating. (Julia Roberts)
4 was make Titanic. (Leonardo DiCaprio)
5 is the Academy Awards. (Sean Penn)
6 is play tennis. (Anna Kournikova)

a	b	c	d	e	f
3					

6 Rewrite the sentences beginning with the words given.

a) I wouldn't want to be written about in the tabloid papers.
   What I wouldn't want _is to be written about in the tabloid papers._

b) He's only well-known in the north of Canada.
   It's only _____
   _____

c) I really hate the way that celebrities always sound so sure of themselves.
   What I really _____
   _____

d) Being on TV is the only thing that matters to some people.
   The only thing _____
   _____

e) I don't understand why people take her so seriously.
   What I _____
   _____

f) I don't like the film, but I do like the soundtrack.
   It isn't the _____
   _____

g) John McCain didn't beat Barack Obama in the presidential election. Obama beat McCain.
   It wasn't _____
   _____
   _____

7 Complete the sentences so that they are true for you.

a) What I'm interested in doing in the future is
   _____
   _____

b) The hardest thing I've ever had to do was
   _____
   _____

c) What I'd enjoy most about being famous is
   _____
   _____

d) What I like least about not being famous is
   _____
   _____

Vocabulary

1 **Match the words in bold with the definitions 1–8.**

a) He **glanced** over his shoulder nervously.

b) She lay on the bed **gazing** up at the ceiling.

c) I **eyed up** her boots for a while before asking her where she'd bought them.

d) As she went out she **caught sight of** herself in the mirror.

e) Stop that! Don't you know it's rude to **stare**?

f) A good teacher can **spot** a talented child.

g) It was then that I first **noticed** him, standing in the corner, looking over at me.

h) I could just about **make out** the writing on the side of the bag.

1 see something for a short time
2 look at something or someone in order to form an opinion of them
3 look at something for a long time, for example because it is attractive or interesting, or because you're thinking of something else
4 look somewhere quickly and then look away
5 see someone or something with difficulty
6 become conscious of someone or something by seeing, hearing or feeling
7 see something and be able to identify it correctly
8 look at someone or something very directly for a long time

a	b	c	d	e	f	g	h
4							

2 **Look at the verbs in bold. Tick the ones that are correct. Change the ones that are wrong.**

a) I **made out** his face for a split second as he walked past.

   I caught sight of his face

b) She **stared at** me across the room.

   _____

c) I couldn't **glance at** the details in the photograph because the quality was so bad.

   _____

d) He was **eyeing up** the girls at the bar.

   _____

e) I **caught sight of** the rain through the window for ages, thinking about what I'd say to her.

   _____

f) He's really good at **spotting** mistakes.

   _____

g) I could just about **make out** his face in the crowd.

   _____

h) Sh! They won't **gaze at** us if we just stand here and keep quiet.

   _____

3 **Cross out the noun in each group that does *not* collocate with the word in bold.**

a) **advertising**   agency   ~~confidence~~   industry

b) **brand**   awareness   identity   tag

c) **consumer**   choice   cut   goods

d) **market**   conference   leader   research

e) **price**   image   index   war

f) **sales**   figures   rep   sector

4 **Underline the correct collocation.**

a) There has been a 20% fall in consumer **products** / spending over the last three months.

b) Can I see the price list / rise, please? I need to know how much this toy costs.

c) The company made more than $20 million in advertising **revenue** / **executive** last year.

d) The sales **team** / **targets** have been working incredibly hard this quarter.

e) I don't believe in paying extra for a brand **loyalty** / **name** when you can get the same thing without a logo for half the price.

f) They were forced to sell their house for much less than its real market **forces** / **value**.

5 **Complete the sentences with the words in the box. Make any changes necessary.**

conjure up   care less   epitomise
fiercely   fussy   haunting   heart-throb
nostalgically   rugged   ~~strip off~~

a) He ___*stripped off*___ , threw his clothes to the ground and ran into the sea.

b) He's a really _____ eater. He won't touch vegetables and he hates fish.

c) I really couldn't _____ about what you think. I'm going to do it anyway.

d) The world of advertising is _____ competitive.

e) Dior perfume adverts _____ all that is chic in French fashion.

f) All the girls loved his _____ good looks. He was a _____ and a heart-breaker.

g) The two old men sat on the bench and talked _____ about the good old days.

h) A young woman sat in the corner playing a _____ tune on her flute, _____ images of deserted beaches.

6 Insert the missing letters to complete the texts.

In an economic crisis a fast food restaurant can be a real cash (1) c*o w* . People cut (2) b_ _k on eating out in expensive restaurants, and although a burger and chips is a (3) f_ _ cry from a romantic candlelit dinner in a posh restaurant, it's much cheaper. Which means the burger bars and the drive-ins are (4) r_ _ _ng in huge profits, while everyone else is tightening their belts.

Product (5) p_ _ _ _m_ _t is a marketing tool. Products such as cars, watches, drinks, etc are 'placed' in films and TV shows as a subtle form of advertising. And when the film is likely to be a box (6) o_ _ _c_ hit, the companies are willing to pay vast sums of money for the (7) p_ _v_ _ _ g_ .

In 2008 Chelsea Football Club became the first football club to (8) s_ _ _k_ a deal with YouTube to allow footage of football games to appear on the website. They made it (9) c_ _ _r , however, that the deal could only be made on (10) c_ _d_ _ _ _n that no live footage could be shown.

7 Tick (✓) the sentences that are correct. Put a cross (✗) next to the sentences that are wrong and underline the mistake.

a) I get <u>absolutely nervous</u> before exams. ✗

b) That was a totally ridiculous thing to say! ✓

c) His performance was very extraordinary.

d) That was definitely one of the best films I've ever seen. It was totally good.

e) I'm sorry, but I thought that was really very boring!

f) Have you seen this video clip? It's absolutely amazing!

g) The film was quite disappointing, but the party afterwards was extremely brilliant.

h) I was terribly disappointed by the reviews. They were really quite dreadful.

i) That was some horror movie. I was very frightened to death.

j) Did you think so? I was extremely bored stiff.

8 Complete the conversation with the words in the box.

complete	entire	~~expectations~~	hype
letdown	disillusioned	utter	waste

A: So, did the film live up to your (1) _expectations_ ?

B: Well, not really. I mean there'd been so much (2) _____ beforehand. But I wasn't totally (3) _____ either. I mean, the acting's pretty good, I certainly wouldn't say it was a complete (4) _____ of time as some reviewers have been saying.

A: So, will you be recommending it to your friends?

B: Probably not!

A: What about you, Carla? What did you think of the film?

C: Don't ask! I thought it was (5) _____ rubbish. I've never seen anything so ridiculous in my (6) _____ life. If you ask me it was a (7) _____ waste of time. Don't see it – it's a massive (8) _____ !

A: Thank you!

🌐 42 Listen and check.

Pronunciation

1 How do you think the following words are pronounced in English?

Adidas	Coca Cola	Heineken	Levis
McDonald's	Nike	Nivea	Nokia	Perrier
Renault	Speedo	Slazenger	Volkswagen

🌐 43 Listen and check.

2 🌐 44 Listen to the recording. Which sentence do you hear first? Number the sentences 1 or 2.

a) My friend, whose mum is French, is bilingual.
My friend whose mum is French is bilingual.

b) She bought me an expensive tie, which I didn't like.
She bought me an expensive tie which I didn't like.

c) My brother, who lives in Rome, is a model.
My brother who lives in Rome is a model.

Listen again and practise saying the sentences after the recording.

Listening

1   🌐 45 Cover the listening script oppposite and listen to seven short voicemail messages. Match them to the small ads below.

1	2	3	4	5	6	7
C						

A **CAR SHARE.** I'm driving London – Paris at the end of this month. Do you want to share petrol expenses and ferry crossing? Call Dan 8540 6927.

B **KENSINGTON.** Close to Underground and shops. Medium room £250 per week, available now. Non-smoking female preferred. 8317 5246.

C **PEUGEOT PARTNER,** 2004, blue, 50,000 miles, well maintained, perfect condition. 1st owner. £5,000 or near offer. Tel 7163 5097.

D **PROFESSIONAL CATERERS,** for all occasions. We offer a wide range of catering services, from basic buffets to wedding parties. For information Tel/fax 7329 8440.

E **PROFESSIONAL GERMAN MALE** seeks friendly international people to share a flat starting December. 8620 5791. Ask for Hans.

F **RETIRED AND LONELY** salesman, but with warm heart, generous and not too bad-looking for my age. Can I take you out? Tel 8930 6613.

G **FILIPINA LADY SEEKS** domestic job, childcare, cleaning, ironing, daily or part-time. Good references. Please call 8751 6047.

2   Listen again. Write the numbers of the calls next to the statements.

a)   The caller doesn't leave a number _3_ , ____ , ____

b)   The caller doesn't give their name ____

c)   The caller is an older person ____ , ____

d)   The caller is going to try again later ____ , ____

3   Look at the script and find:

a)   Four ways of asking someone to return your call

_____

_____

_____

_____

1
Erm, yes, hello, my name's Vic, Vic Richards, and I'm interested in the car you've got for sale. Perhaps you could give me a call on my mobile? The number's 0797 532488.

2
Good evening. The name's Ferguson, Reginald Ferguson, and I'm calling about your advertisement. I wonder if you would be ready to give me a quote for my daughter's wedding? Eighty guests, buffet dinner, full works, best you can do. Perhaps you could give my secretary a call on 0207 7491 2598. Thank you.

3
Hello. This is Vivienne Redman here. I'm looking for someone who would be able to pick up my little ones from their nursery in Knightsbridge on Tuesday and Friday afternoons. Do you have a driving licence? I'll try again later.

4
Uh, I've never done this before, but you sound like a gentleman. I used to be in sales, too, before I retired, that is, and I was wondering if, maybe, I could take *you* out. I never know what to do with my money since my Dennis died. It would be my special treat. My name's Mary and my number is 423 7799.

5
Hallo, bonjour. I am Sophie, and I am also looking for some persons with whom to share an apartment in the centre of town. I am staying in the Rochester Hotel. Could you please call me back there? Thank you.

6
Dan? Hi, my name's Hannah and I have to go over to France in a couple of weeks. Could you give me a call back? How much do you think it'll come to? Oh, my number's 650 7861. Cheers!

7
I'm calling about the ad and I'm wondering if I can come round to have a look at the flat. Is it near South Kensington or High Street Kensington? Er ... I'll call again in half a hour, OK?

b)   Two ways of saying you'll call again

_____

_____

c)   Three ways of explaining the reason for your call

_____

_____

_____

Writing

Writing a film review
Punctuation

1 Read the film review opposite. Match the paragraph numbers to the following paragraph summaries.

Recommendation
Cast
Basic information
Plot

paragraph 1 _____

paragraph 2 _____

paragraph 3 _____

paragraph 4 _____

2 Find words and phrases in the text (in italics) that are the *opposite* of the following.

a) weak

b) his acting is not very good

c) definitely not worth seeing

d) is not for all tastes

e) is unpopular with the critics

f) you won't like it

3 The following sentences all come from film reviews. Punctuate them.

a) The soundtrack mostly songs by the brilliant A. R. Rahman is worth buying on CD

b) Danny Boyle the director of the film also made *The Beach* and *28 Days Later*

c) As in Boyles other films the special effects play an important part

d) Based on a novel by Vikas Swarup the screenplay was written by Simon Beaufoy the writer of *The Full Monty*

e) The ending which is no surprise is the stuff of fairy tales

f) Hollywood melodrama said one critic but the film is much more than that

4 Choose a film that you have seen recently. Write a short review of the film, giving your opinion of it. You should write approximately 180 words.

Here are some questions that will help you.

What kind of film is it? (comedy, romance, etc.)

When was it released?

Was it a hit at the box office?

What sort of people will like it?

What kind of reviews has it had?

Where is it set?

What is (un)interesting about the plot?

Are there any particularly memorable scenes?

What are the best/worst features of the film? (acting, script, camerawork, costumes, sets, special effects, etc.)

Who stars in it?

ONE TO WATCH –
Slumdog Millionaire

Slumdog Millionaire is *one of the best movies I've seen for a long time.* Released in 2008, this *powerful* romantic drama *has received rave reviews* and won eight Oscars in 2009.

It tells the gripping story of a young man from the slums of Mumbai who takes part in the Indian version of the TV competition 'Who Wants to be a Millionaire?'. He needs to answer just one more question to win the jackpot, but the recording of the show stops for the night. Jamal must return the next day, but he is arrested by the police for cheating. We learn the story of his life in flashbacks.

Dev Patel stars in the role of Jamal, the boy from the slums, and *his performance is worthy of an Oscar.* Freida Pinto plays Latika, the love of Jamal's life. However, the real star of the film is the city of Mumbai, the modern city where the film is set.

Slumdog Millionaire is a 'feel-good' movie that *will appeal to everyone* – but be prepared for some scenes that are difficult to watch. If you haven't seen it yet, see it soon. *You won't be disappointed.*

11 Student

Grammar

1 Underline the correct verb form.

a) How well do you think you <u>will do</u> / **are doing** in the exam tomorrow?

b) I'm **failing** / **going to fail** the English exam if I **don't** / **won't** get some work done!

c) Some friends **will come** / **are coming** round to my house tonight to do some revision.

d) Once the exam **has started** / **will start**, no-one **might be** / **will be** allowed to leave the room.

e) **Will anyone try** / **Is anyone trying** to cheat in the exam tomorrow?

f) They **will** / **might** – it depends if they get the chance.

h) We **will have** / **are going to have** a party once the exams **will be** / **are** over.

i) I **wait** /**'m going to wait** until I **know** / **will know** my results before I go on holiday.

2 There is one mistake in each sentence. Find the mistakes and correct them.

a) I'm going to study every single day until the exams ~~will~~ have finished.

b) By the end of May I'll be finishing all my exams.

c) I'm going to take some time off before I'm looking for a job.

d) We're all going to go to France as soon as the term is finishing.

e) We might camp unless the weather will have changed.

f) By July I will probably spend all my money.

g) If my parents aren't giving me some money, I'll have to find a job.

3 Complete the sentences so that they are true for you. Use the verb phrases in the box to help you.

apply for university   buy a (new) car
finish my studies   get married
get a (new) job   go travelling
have children   leave home
move house   pass my driving test
pass my exam   speak fluently

a) I'm not going to _____ until _____

b) By the end of the year I _____ _____

c) I'll stop studying English when _____ _____

d) I'll definitely _____ before I _____

e) I'll _____ as soon as I _____

Pronunciation

1 Underline the word in each group that contains the vowel sound.

a) /ɪ/   last, least, list
b) /iː/   feel, fill, full
c) /ʊ/   back, bake, book
d) /uː/   seen, soon, sun
e) /e/   had, head, heard
f) /ɜː/   lane, lean, learn
g) /ɔː/   case, course, kiss
h) /æ/   fan, fin, fun
i) /ʌ/   bars, bees, buzz
j) /ɑː/   heart, hot, hurt
k) /ɒ/   want, weren't, won't

🔊 46 **Listen and check.**

2 Write the phonetic symbol of the vowel in the words below.

a) best _____   g) pop _____
b) dream _____   h) run _____
c) first _____   i) school _____
d) gap _____   j) sort _____
e) good _____   k) thing _____
f) mark _____

Vocabulary

1 **Complete the text with the words in the box.**

applied	course	failed	further
grant	heart	marks	~~pay~~

When I was at school I just wasn't interested. I
didn't (1) ___pay___ attention to the teachers and I
was really bad at learning things by (2) _____ .
I always got low (3) _____ and there was no
way I was going to go on to (4) _____ education.
In the last year I (5) _____ all my exams, so I
left school and got a job as a waitress. It was hard
work, but I liked earning my own money and after
a couple of years I decided to take a (6) _____
in catering at a local college. I really enjoyed it and
found that for the first time I was doing really well.
So at the end of the course I (7) _____ for a place
at university to study hotel management. I was so
pleased when I got a place – and even more pleased
when I managed to get a (8) _____ ! Five years
later and here I am, running my own hotel!

🌐 **47 Listen and check.**

2 **Complete the second sentence so that it means the same as the first.**

a) It is not thought that he will study very hard.
It is unlikely *that he will study very hard.*

b) He will probably fail most of his exams.
It is likely _____
_____

c) He'll definitely turn up without a pen.
He's bound _____
_____

d) He's sure to try and cheat.
It's inevitable _____
_____

e) He's likely to end up at the bottom of the class.
It's probable _____
_____

f) People don't think he'll go on to university.
He's not expected _____
_____

g) He's unlikely to get a good job.
It's unlikely _____
_____

h) It's certain that he will get into trouble with the police.
He's bound to _____
_____

3 **Insert the missing letters. The first letter of each word has been given to you.**

a) I got my first t*a s t e* of freedom when I went travelling on my own for the first time.

b) It's always good to have a qualification b_ _ _ _ _ you.

c) I really needed to travel. I just had to get it out of my s_ _ _ _ _ .

d) Have you come to your s_ _ _ _ _ at last?

e) It's hard to m_ _ _ it in the world of cinema.

f) We can't really help her very much. It's all u_ t_ h_ _ and what she wants to do.

4 **Underline the correct word. Then match the expressions with the adjectives in the box.**

afraid	amazed	~~amazing~~	desperate
exhausted	happy	ill	sad
thirsty	worried		

a) It was **head-blowing** / **mind-blowing**
amazing

b) I was going out of my **mind** / **thoughts**
_____

c) I was over the **moon** / **sun** _____

d) I was on my last **breath** / **legs** _____

e) I **fell** / **burst** into tears _____

f) I was at the end of my **rope** / **tether**
_____

g) It took my **breath** / **legs** away _____

h) I was **dying** / **starving** for a drink _____

i) I was at death's **door** / **gate** _____

j) I was scared **solid** / **stiff** _____

5 **Write true answers to the job interview questions. Use the phrases in the box.**

always been interested in	ready / willing to
take steps to	very keen to	well-suited to

a) What would you say is your greatest weakness?
_____
_____

b) What are your greatest strengths?
_____
_____

c) What would you like to be doing in five years' time?
_____
_____

d) What are your long-term objectives?
_____
_____

Reading

1 ◉ 48 Read the first section of the poem (lines 1–12) and choose the correct answer for the questions.

1 Where are the poet and the person he is speaking to?
   a) in a teachers' room
   b) at someone's house
   c) in a restaurant

2 Who is 'he'?
   a) the poet
   b) one of the dinner guests

3 What does 'he' think of teaching?
   a) that it doesn't pay very well
   b) that it's a good option

4 What does 'he' want to know?
   a) what the poet teaches
   b) how much money he makes

2 Read the rest of the poem and answer these questions.

a) What and who does the poet teach?

b) Do you think he's a good teacher?

c) Does he enjoy his job? Why / Why not?

3 Look at the whole poem again and match the definitions below to the words in bold (1–10).

a) the highest military honour awarded by the American government __4__

b) completed copies of a piece of writing ____

c) expression: decide not to say something ____

d) American: a time and place set aside for children to do their homework supervised by a teacher ____

e) informal, can be offensive: used for emphasising what you are saying, especially when you are angry or annoyed ____

f) not write something correctly ____

g) informal: child ____

h) express anger to someone in a very rude way by holding up your longest finger ____

i) American, very informal, impolite: telling someone what you think in a very assertive and, possibly, aggressive way ____

j) American: short for 'mathematics', in British English the expression is *maths* ____

What Teachers Make, or Objection Overruled, or If things don't work out, you can always go to law school

By Taylor Mali

He says the problem with teachers is, "What's a **kid** (1) going to
   learn from someone who decided his best option in life was to
   become a teacher?"
He reminds the other dinner guests that it's true what they say about
   teachers:
Those who can, do; those who can't, teach.

I decide to **bite my tongue** (2) instead of his
   and resist the temptation to remind the other dinner guests that
   it's also true what they say about lawyers.

Because we're eating, after all, and this is polite company.

"I mean, you're a teacher, Taylor," he says.
"Be honest. What do you make?"

And I wish he hadn't done that
(asked me to be honest)
because, you see, I have a policy
about honesty and **ass-kicking** (3):
if you ask for it, I have to let you have it.

You want to know what I make?

I make kids work harder than they ever thought they could.
I can make a C+ feel like a **Congressional medal of honor** (4)
and an A– feel like a slap in the face.
How dare you waste my time with anything less than your very best.

I make kids sit through 40 minutes of **study hall** (5)
in absolute silence. No, you may not work in groups.
No, you may not ask a question.
Why won't I let you get a drink of water?
Because you're not thirsty, you're bored, that's why.

I make parents tremble in fear when I call home:
I hope I haven't called at a bad time,
I just wanted to talk to you about something Billy said today.
Billy said, "Leave the kid alone. I still cry sometimes, don't you?"
And it was the noblest act of courage I have ever seen.

I make parents see their children for who they are
and what they can be.

You want to know what I make?

I make kids wonder,
I make them question.
I make them criticize.
I make them apologize and mean it.
I make them write, write, write.
And then I make them read.
I make them spell definitely beautiful, definitely beautiful, definitely beautiful
over and over and over again until they will never **misspell** (6)
either one of those words again.
I make them show all their work in **math** (7).
And hide it on their **final drafts** (8) in English.
I make them understand that if you got this (brains)
then you follow this (heart) and if someone ever tries to judge you
by what you make, you **give them this (the finger).** (9)

Let me break it down for you, so you know what I say is true:
I make a **goddamn** (10) difference! What about you?

Writing

Writing a letter of application
Formal expressions
Appropriacy

1 Find seven pairs of phrases in the list below which mean approximately the same. In each pair, mark one phrase F (formal) and one phrase I (informal).

1 *a (F) n (I)*   5 _____

2 _____   6 _____

3 _____   7 _____

4 _____

a) as advertised in the newspaper
b) drop us a line soon
c) I am not at all bad at
d) I enclose a copy of my CV
e) I feel I am well-suited to this position because
f) I have a good standard of
g) I look forward to hearing from you
h) I quite fancy being a
i) I would like to apply for the post of
j) I've stuck in a copy of my CV for you to have a look at
k) my previous experience includes
l) over the years, I have also
m) the job looks just right for me because
n) which I saw in the paper

2 A letter of application typically has four parts:

1 reason for writing
2 factual information about the applicant
3 information about personality and interests
4 information about availability and conclusion

Decide which formal expressions in Exercise 1 would probably be in this type of letter and which part of the letter (1–4) they would be in.

Part 1 Expressions ☐ ☐
Part 2 Expressions ☐ ☐
Part 3 Expressions ☐
Part 4 Expressions ☐ ☐

3 In the letter extract below, cross out any information which it would not be appropriate to include in a job application.

I was born in a small village not far from Eindhoven, so my mother tongue is Dutch, but I have a good standard of spoken and written English, because I have been going to an excellent language school near my town and I have been to America four times in my holidays. I also had an Irish girlfriend for a couple of weeks.

I have an international driving licence and I currently drive a red convertible Audi. I was going to work for a travel company here in the Netherlands last year, but in the end I worked for two months at the help desk at Schiphol Airport, where I had to deal with people from all over the world, and sometimes I got to drive one of the airport buggies if there was a disabled passenger who needed some help. It was great fun.

4 Look at the advertisement below, which comes from an English newspaper.

International Travel Organisation

We are looking for young, friendly and patient staff to work in July and August in London. If you have the right profile, you will be responsible for meeting our clients at Heathrow and Gatwick airports and accompanying them to their accommodation in central London.

No previous experience necessary.

Good level of English and one other language required.

Driving licence an advantage but not essential.

We offer a generous salary and will provide a flat share near our offices in Kings Cross.

If you are interested in this post, please send a CV and accompanying letter to: Eleanor.gibbon@ITO.org

Make a note in the boxes below of information you would include in paragraphs 2 and 3 of your letter of application for this job.

Paragraph 2

```



```

Paragraph 3

```



```

5 Write your letter of application in about 180 words in an appropriate style.

Grammar

1 **Underline the correct form.**

a) I have a small desk by a window **overlooked** / **overlooking** the street.

b) Out of the window, I can see a lot of people **walked** / **walking** in the street.

c) In the kitchen, there is a photo of me **taken** / **taking** on holiday last year.

d) I like to spend time in the living room **watched** / **watching** TV.

e) The room, **cleaned** / **cleaning** only recently, is already untidy.

f) My bookshelves are full of unopened books **read** / **reading** by no one.

g) I hate my bathroom – **located** / **locating** at the back of the flat, it's very cold.

2 **Complete the text with the correct participle form of the verb in brackets.**

(1) _____Sitting_____ (sit) in my penthouse suite on the 76th floor, I have a wonderful view of the city and of the ships (2) _____ (go) up and down the river. My company headquarters, (3) _____ (occupy) the other 75 floors, are conveniently placed under my feet, and the whole building is a landmark in the city, (4) _____ (admire) by architects around the world. (5) _____ (fit) with all the latest energy-saving devices, the building has won many awards. As I am the owner of a company (6) _____ (specialise) in green forms of energy and (7) _____ (know) for its interest in the environment, I am naturally very happy with my home.

🌐 **49 Listen and check.**

3 **Complete the text with the words in the box.**

all	enough	few	hardly	little	~~many~~
most	no	none	plenty	several	

There can't be (1) ___many___ places as boring as Ruislip (zone 6 on the London Underground). There used to be (2) _____ cinemas and a (3) _____ youth clubs, but now there are almost (4) _____ facilities for younger people. Sure, there are (5) _____ of things you can do if you have a car, but you have very (6) _____ choice if you haven't got wheels. There are (7) _____ any of my friends left – (8) _____ of them moved on when they had (9) _____ money. (10) _____ of them would ever go back there. Now that they are middle-aged, they (11) _____ seem happy living in a similar place on the other side of London.

4 **Some of the lines in the text below are correct, and some have a word which should not be there. If a line is correct, put a tick (✓) next to it. If not, cross out the unnecessary word.**

a) Osgood, Indiana, isn't the most ~~of~~ exciting

b) place in the world to grow up. There was not

c) hardly anything to do and there were

d) few other kids to play with. In any case, none

e) of the other kids had much of time to play

f) because they had to help their families, while

g) I had far too much time. Ma had died when I

h) was young, and Pop had no the time for kids.

i) I dreamt of escaping to the big city and the

j) several months after my 18th birthday, I left.

Pronunciation

🌐 **50 Listen and repeat the phrases and notice how the underlined words are pronounced with a schwa sound /ə/.**

a) get out <u>of</u> bed, the middle <u>of</u> nowhere

b) come <u>and</u> stay, light <u>and</u> bright

c) leave <u>at</u> short notice, time <u>at</u> home

d) a quarter <u>to</u> six, good <u>to</u> see you

e) opportunities <u>for</u> young people, thanks <u>for</u> everything

Vocabulary

1 **Complete the sentences with one word from box A and one word from box B.**

A

| central | fireworks | fossil |
| pitch | ~~pop~~ | street |

B

| cred | dark | display | fuels |
| heating | ~~next door~~ |

a) I'm just going to _____*pop next door*_____ for a chat.

b) The world cannot afford to rely on
   _____ .

c) Bills for _____ , both gas and electricity, are rising fast.

d) He was a lot more interested in his _____ than in doing his studies.

e) The New Year began with a fantastic _____ .

f) Deep underground, the explorers found themselves in the _____ when their lights failed.

2 **Put the word tiles in order to make 10 breakfast foods.**

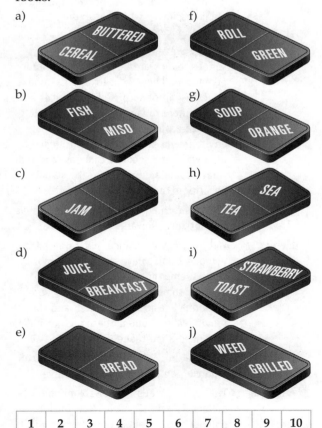

a) BUTTERED CEREAL

f) ROLL GREEN

b) FISH MISO

g) SOUP ORANGE

c) JAM

h) SEA TEA

d) JUICE BREAKFAST

i) STRAWBERRY TOAST

e) BREAD

j) WEED GRILLED

1	2	3	4	5	6	7	8	9	10
e	f								c

3 **Number the lines in the correct order to make a conversation.**

☐ Give me a ring some time, OK?

☐ Good to see you, too. Thanks for coming.

☐ I will. Give my regards to Betty, will you? Bye.

☐ My pleasure. Thank you for inviting me.

1 Well, I'd better be going. It was really good to see you.

4 **Complete the sentences with words from the word square.**

D	O	O	R	M	A	T	S	I	L	L
J	R	B	R	U	S	H	U	M	O	P
Y	N	T	I	L	E	S	T	C	K	C
M	A	N	T	L	E	P	I	E	C	E
D	M	L	P	C	P	A	L	B	L	G
U	E	A	O	P	O	R	I	O	B	L
S	N	T	R	E	I	Q	T	L	L	A
T	T	C	C	G	N	U	Y	T	I	Z
P	S	H	H	Z	T	E	P	W	N	I
A	R	R	Q	F	I	T	T	E	D	N
N	C	E	L	L	A	R	B	U	S	G
H	O	O	K	X	V	W	L	O	F	T

a) A *cellar* is a good place to keep wine.

b) People often store things in their _ _ _ _ or _ _ _ _ _ _ _ room.

c) Some houses have a _ _ _ _ _ so that people don't get wet when they are at the front door.

d) You can use a _ _ _ _ _ _ _ and _ _ _ _ _ or a _ _ _ for cleaning.

e) Most people's floors are _ _ _ _ _ _ _ _ , _ _ _ _ _ or _ _ _ _ _ _ carpets.

f) You wipe your feet on the _ _ _ _ _ _ _ when you go into someone's home.

g) Offices usually have _ _ _ _ _ _ rather than curtains.

h) Double-_ _ _ _ _ _ _ keeps a room warm.

i) Some people put flowers outside on the window _ _ _ _ .

j) It's safer to slide the _ _ _ _ across the door at night.

k) You sometimes find a _ _ _ _ _ _ _ _ _ _ _ with _ _ _ _ _ _ _ _ on it above a fireplace.

l) You can hang things up on a _ _ _ _ or a _ _ _ .

m) You can plug in an electrical appliance at the power _ _ _ _ _ .

Listening

1 🌐 51 **Cover the listening script opposite. Listen to a radio feature about an auction in California and answer the questions.**

a) What is being sold?

_____

b) How many people are taking part in the auction?

_____

c) How many different kinds of property are on sale?

_____

d) In what ways are these properties 'fully secure'?

_____

e) How much is the first property sold for?

_____

2 **Listen again and say if the sentences are true (*T*) or false (*F*).**

a) The auction is taking place in the centre of Los Angeles. ☐

b) The houses are in the centre of Malibu. ☐

c) People have to pay extra for things like swimming pools and saunas. ☐

d) The male reporter would like to buy one of the houses. ☐

e) People want to buy houses on estates that have high security. ☐

f) Eleni thinks it will be difficult for some buyers to get a mortgage. ☐

3 **Find words or phrases in the recording script to match the definitions.**

a) pushed or squeezed _____

b) connections _____

c) most fashionable _____

d) extremely rich _____

e) carrying a gun _____

Auctioneer:	Ten million dollars, eleven, twelve, thirteen, fourteen, fifteen, we have fifteen million dollars, and a half, sixteen, and a half, seventeen ...
Reporter:	There are over four hundred people crammed into the auction house here in downtown L.A. where I am now standing. On top of that, it's believed that as many as four hundred more are following the bidding on the phone or on Internet link-ups.
Auctioneer:	Nineteen, and a half, twenty, twenty million dollars, twenty million, one, do I have two, twenty-two ...
Reporter:	These are the first homes to be sold in a new residential development just north of Malibu, but what makes people ready to pay such prices? Well, there are four types of villa being sold today. Buyers can choose between the English country house, the Tuscan villa, the French Louis XIV chateau or a Manhattan style loft. All of them come with the basic necessities: swimming pools, jacuzzis, saunas, gyms, you name it. And they're all fully furnished, down to the smallest details: beautiful rugs from the hippest young designers, exotic indoor plants from the Honduran rainforest, or the Picasso-inspired curtains. Despite the difficult economic times that we are living in, it seems that some people are not short of a buck or two. I asked Eleni Vassilakis, who is attending the auction, for her reactions.
Eleni:	Hi. Yes, we're talking about some pretty serious real estate here. This is luxury for people who know what luxury is. To be honest, I'm not surprised that prices are so high here today. Remember that all of these properties are in a fully secure environment, the estate is surrounded by high walls and security cameras, and that's what people are looking for these days. Security is the word.
Reporter:	The whole thing looks like a prison to me. I'm not sure I'd want to live there.
Eleni:	Well, that's your choice, but I guess that you and I don't have that kind of money! We're seeing more and more of these estates, some of them guarded by dogs and armed security personnel, and they're proving very popular. These are not people who need a mortgage!
Reporter:	From Malibu, California, this is Jo Wilson reporting on how the other half live.
Auctioneer:	Twenty-six, that's twenty-six million dollars. Twenty-six. Sold. Now for lot number two, a Palladian style villa with eleven bedrooms ...

Writing

Writing a description of a holiday home
Linking words
Lexical variety: adjectives, adverbs and verbs

1 Read the description below and match the topics to the paragraphs.

a) appearance ☐
b) facilities ☐
c) interior ☐
d) location ☐

1 My ideal holiday home would be a *nice* house on the north coast of Cornwall in the south-west of England. It would be near a *nice* beach and, on top of that, have a very *nice* little place for my *nice* private yacht.

2 It would be an old-fashioned house and have *nice* flowers climbing the walls. Above all, I would want *big* windows so lots of light could get in. There would be a *very nice big* garden with fruit trees and perhaps a *nice* little pond. In addition, it would have a *nice* swimming pool at the back.

3 Inside, the rooms would be *big*. They would be painted in *nice* pastel colours and there would be some *nice* furniture, but not too much, so that the rooms would feel even *bigger* as a result. I would put *nice* plants everywhere to make the place feel warm and I would have some *nice* pictures on the walls.

4 A *nice* kitchen would be *very* important for me. Incidentally, the house would also have to *have* lots of rooms for my friends to stay. Other than that, I wouldn't want very much – apart from the swimming pool of course. Finally, the house would have a sauna so I could relax at the end of a *very* tiring day of doing nothing.

2 Replace the words in italics in Exercise 1 with words from the four boxes.

attractive beautiful charming elegant magnificent picturesque pretty stunning tasteful

fair-sized immense roomy spacious

exceptionally extremely incredibly particularly remarkably

boast contain include possess

3 Now write a description of your ideal holiday home. You should write about 180 words. Use some of these linking words/phrases.

Above all alternatively as a result finally however in addition incidentally on top of that to begin with other than that

Story: *Magnetism*
By F. Scott Fitzgerald, retold by Margaret Tarner

The wide street was very pleasant. Its fine big houses were smart and modern. Everything looked clean and bright in the California sunshine.

A young Mexican maid was slowly sweeping the steps of the biggest house on the street. Dolores worked for Mr and Mrs Hannaford. She had a good job.

Mr Hannaford's driver was waiting in the car outside. Dolores looked back into the house. Mr Hannaford would be coming out soon. At that moment, he appeared at the front door and smiled at Dolores.

George Hannaford was a movie-star. He was young and very handsome. His smile confused Dolores so much, that she fell down a step.

'I hope you haven't hurt yourself,' George Hannaford said in a worried voice. He put out his hand to help her, but the young girl had already stood up.

'Are you sure you're all right?'

'Oh, sure.'

'I'm terribly sorry.'

'Oh, you didn't do anything, it wasn't your fault.'

George Hannaford walked quickly down the steps and got into his car. Dolores gazed after him. For a moment, she thought about having a love affair with him. Then she sighed and got on with her work.

George Hannaford went first to Jules Rennard's house. The two men were good friends. They were both gentle, simple men. In the crazy world of Hollywood, they both knew that good friends were important.

'I want to go fishing,' George said. 'When will you be able to go? I'm taking the boat to Lower California.'

Jules was delighted with the idea. He wanted to go away very much because he had just been divorced. He wanted to get away from women for a time.

'How's your baby?' Jules asked.

'Fine.'

'And Kay?'

'Kay's not happy. She's jealous.'

'Jealous?' Jules repeated. 'Who's she jealous of?'

'Helen Avery. But Kay's got nothing to worry about. I'm not in love with Helen Avery.'

'I must go. I'm late. Let me know when you can come fishing.'

George drove on into the hills behind the city. His driver stopped at the gates of the film studios and George got out of the car. He walked on until he came to a door marked 'Schroeder'.

'Is anyone with Mr Schroeder?' George asked as he walked into the office.

'No, Mr Hannaford,' said a secretary. 'He's in his room, on the phone.'

George's eyes turned to a young lady working at a desk.

'Hello, Margaret. How are you?' George said.

Miss Margaret Donovan, a script-girl, had been his friend for many years.

'Hello, George. These are the changes to the script that we decided on, on Thursday night. I need your signature. Can you sign the changes?'

'Very well, darling.'

George looked admiringly at Margaret Donovan's delicate, beautiful face. Why had she never gone into the movies? he wondered.

As George finished signing the papers, Pete Schroeder opened his door.

'George, come inside!' he said excitedly. 'There's someone on the phone. I want you to listen to what they have to say.'

Hannaford followed Pete into his office.

'Pick up the phone and say "hello",' Pete said. 'Don't say who you are.'

'Hello,' George said, into the phone.

'Who is this?' asked a girl's voice.

'Who do you want to speak to?' George asked.

'To George Hannaford,' the girl said. 'Is this him?'

'Yes.'

'Oh, George, it's me – Gwen. It's been difficult finding you.'

'Gwen who?' George asked quickly.

'Gwen, from San Francisco … last Thursday night.'

'I'm sorry, there must be some mistake. I don't know you.'

'There's no mistake if you're George Hannaford,' the voice said sharply. 'This is Gwen Becker. You spent last Thursday evening with me in San Francisco. You know who I am!'

Schroeder took the phone from George's hand and hungup.

'Somebody in San Francisco has been saying he's me,' George said. 'These girls never believe they've been tricked. What's happening, Pete?'

'Let's go over to the set and see.'

As George and Pete walked along, everyone turned to look at George. He was so handsome. And what a charming smile he had!

On the set, a pretty girl was talking to somebody in a low, angry voice. Her name was Helen Avery and she was eighteen.

George Hannaford had been thinking about Helen Avery for two weeks. He had made sure that she was in a film with him. They were together all day and every day. And now his wife, Kay, was jealous.

So George had decided he would forget about Helen Avery. He did not want to end his successful marriage. He decided to turn off the magnetism that attracted every woman to him.

George and Helen were on the set all afternoon. When the filming was over, they were alone for a moment.

They stared at each other. Helen's face was young and frightened. But George had decided what he was going to do.

'Helen,' he said in a quiet voice, 'I'm very sorry. I love my wife. You and I have to work together. But we can't have an affair.'

The girl suddenly began to cry.

'Have you got a handkerchief?' she said.

George gave her his handkerchief. He stood with her for a time and then turned away and left.

As he was driven home, George wondered when Jules would be able to go fishing.

George was surprised when Kay greeted him coldly when he returned.

'What's the matter?' he asked. 'Are you still cross with me?'

'Did you forget that we've been invited out tonight – to Katherine Davis's party? I didn't know whether you wanted to go. I asked Arthur Busch to take me.'

'I'd like to go,' George said quietly. They ate their dinner in silence. Kay's anger made George feel angry with himself. He stood up. He was about to put his arms around Kay, when the door opened. Dolores, the maid, said that Mr Arthur Busch had arrived.

Busch was an ugly little man, but everyone liked him. He was a successful movie director and had been in love with Kay for many years.

They all went to the party together. Most of the guests were movie-stars. Some of them were very famous. All of them were pleased to see George and Kay. Some of the youngest stars had been invited too and George guessed that Helen Avery would be there. Then he saw her and their eyes met. He was quite sure now that he didn't love her.

He decided to turn off the magnetism that attracted every woman to him.

Helen was very excited. She had just heard that she had got an important part in a movie. She hurried across the room to tell George the news.

'That's wonderful,' George said. 'I'm so glad.'

Helen laughed.

'Oh, we're both such good actors, you and I, George,' she said coldly. 'There should have been a camera to film our scene this afternoon!'

George smiled and said nothing else. Soon they were in the middle of a crowd of people.

Time passed pleasantly. When George thought it was time to go home, he went to get Kay. She had been sitting with Arthur Busch all evening.

Kay had had several drinks and she did not want to leave. After a brief argument with her, George went upstairs to get his coat. When he came downstairs, he was told that Kay had already gone out to the car.

George saw Kay and Arthur Busch standing under a street lamp. They were holding hands and gazing into each other's eyes. George was surprised, but he walked on towards them. Kay and Arthur turned to look at him. They stepped apart from each other slowly.

'Goodbye, Arthur,' George said cheerfully, as he walked with Kay to their car. Soon they were driving through the clear California night.

Kay said nothing. George said nothing. He could not believe what he had seen. Was Kay in love with Arthur? They went up the steps and into their house without speaking.

There was a light on in the library. Kay looked in.

'There's someone in there,' she said. 'I'm going upstairs. Goodnight.'

A young man walked out of the library. He had a pale, hard face.

'Mr Hannaford?' he said. 'I recognize you from your movies.'

'What do you want? I don't know who you are.'

'My name is Donovan. I'm Margaret Donovan's brother. Come into the library for a moment.'

George looked at the young man across the library table.

'Listen, Hannaford, my sister wants fifty thousand dollars,' the young man said, in a hard voice.

'What are you talking about?'

'Margaret wants fifty thousand dollars,' Donovan repeated.

George stared at him.

'Does your sister know you're here?' he asked.

'She sent me. For fifty thousand dollars, she'll give you those letters and say no more about them.'

'Letters? What letters?' George asked, laughing. 'This is a joke, isn't it?' he said. 'Did Schroeder send you?'

'This isn't a joke, Hannaford,' the young man replied. 'I'm talking about those letters you signed this afternoon.'

———

An hour later, George walked slowly upstairs to bed. He had known Margaret Donovan for seven years – they were friends. He had even kissed her once, (but that was before he met Kay).

Donovan did have some letters. They had been typed on the typewriter George kept in the studio. They were love letters and they promised that he would divorce Kay and marry Margaret. George had not written the letters. He had been tricked into signing them that afternoon.

George was very tired and he fell asleep at once. He dreamt about Kay. In his dream Kay was gentle and loving. 'Think how you love me,' she had whispered. 'Always remember how you love me now!'

George woke up suddenly to the sound of the baby crying. It was morning. George tried to think clearly. He must do something about Margaret at once. He must end his quarrel with Kay. That was the most important thing of all.

George phoned his lawyer and asked him to come round to the house. As he put down the phone, it rang again. It was Helen Avery.

'George, I'm calling you about last night. I was so unkind to you.'

'Don't be silly, Helen,' George said, trying to remember what she had said. Then he added, 'It's better not to be friendly to each other.'

'Oh, George, no …' Helen said softly. 'You know how I feel about you. I …'

At that moment, the door opened and Kay came in. She gave her husband a hard little smile.

George saw Kay and Arthur Busch holding hands and gazing into each other's eyes.

STORY Magnetism

'Are you busy?' she said.

'No, no.' George said.

Then he spoke into the phone as he put it down, 'Well, goodbye.'

'I didn't mean to interrupt you,' Kay said coldly.

'You didn't.'

George thought for a moment, then he said, 'That was Helen Avery.'

'I don't care who it was. It makes no difference now. We're through, George. Our marriage is finished. You know it as well as I do.'

'That's silly,' George answered. 'You can't mean you don't love me any more.' He smiled. He was not very worried. They had had quarrels like this before.

'Yes, I do. No. I don't know,' Kay burst into tears. 'Oh, it's so sad,' she said. 'Arthur has cared for me for so long. He's here now, downstairs.'

George stared at her. Kay meant what she had said. Their marriage was finished. This was really happening.

'I've never cared for Helen Avery. I've never cared for anyone but you,' he said.

They went downstairs together. The bright California sun was shining hard and clear as it always did.

There were two men in the living-room. One of them was George's lawyer, Mr Castle. The other was Arthur Busch. His face was sad and white.

George knew what was going to happen. He could see the scene in his mind like a movie. He would stand in front of Kay and Arthur Busch. He would talk, plead, act.

George suddenly decided what to do. He would not take part in that scene. He turned to his lawyer.

'A script-girl called Margaret Donovan is blackmailing me with some letters,' George said. 'She wants fifty thousand dollars. It's all nonsense, of course. I'll come to see you tomorrow.'

Then George walked up to Kay and Arthur and spoke more quietly.

'I don't know what you two want to do,' he said. 'But leave me out of your plan. I don't want to take part in it. None of this is my fault.'

Without another word, George walked out of the house. His car was outside. He got into it.

'Go to Santa Monica,' George told his driver. As he was driven through the bright, clear sunlight, George thought about Kay and Arthur. Kay wanted him to apologize, get down on his knees, plead with her. But George would not. He would not fight against Arthur Busch.

Millions of people had gazed at George's expressive, handsome face on movie screens. So George had become a rich and famous movie star. But he was really a gentle, honest, romantic man. He wanted his marriage to last. Not many marriages did last in Hollywood. George loved Kay, but he had made one mistake. He had looked at Helen Avery and now everything was going wrong.

The car was now passing an apartment house that George recognized.

He had called for Margaret Donovan here, many years ago. Before he had met and married Kay, they had gone to a dance together.

'Stop here!' George said quickly. He had to speak to Margaret.

When she saw George she gave a cry and moved away from the door. George followed her into the apartment.

'I suppose this blackmail was your brother's idea,' George said sadly. 'Do you need the money so badly?'

George looked at Margaret's unhappy face. He felt sorry for her – and for himself.

'May I sit down?' George went on in a tired voice. 'People don't seem to like me today.'

'I thought everyone loved you, George,' Margaret said.

'They don't.'

'Am I the only one who loves you, George? But that can't be true! You are George Hannaford, the great movie-star!'

'That's all nonsense,' George said quietly.

'I suppose I should be glad you are here,' Margaret went on. 'I've dreamt of this scene so many times – you sitting here and me sitting at your feet. But you look tired, George. Were you at a party last night?'

'I was,' George replied. 'And when I got home, your brother was waiting for me. Was it all his idea?'

'We planned it between us. I wanted you to love me, George. I've loved you for years. You can't stop people loving you, can you, George?'

'But I don't want …'

'Yes, I know, George. It's your charm. It makes people come to you – people you aren't interested in. It's not your fault. But you did kiss me, you know.'

George sat very quietly. He had always known that women loved him. But he had thought that their love soon disappeared.

'George,' Margaret was saying, 'you don't know what it's like to love you. Women remember every word, every smile. You smile at everyone, don't you, George? It's part of your charm, your magnetism. It's not your fault.'

George stood up and started to turn away from her.

'I'm boring you,' Margaret said softly. 'You want to go home. But there's just one more thing, George.'

Margaret went to her desk and took out the letters. She looked at them and then tore them into small pieces.

'There you are,' she said. 'Now go!'

'I've loved you for years. You can't stop people loving you, can you, George?'

'Why must I go now? Can't we be friends?'

Margaret burst into tears.

'Oh go – stay – do as you like! I'm yours if you stay. But you could have any woman in the world, couldn't you?'

'Margaret …' George began.

'You'd better go,' Margaret said, turning her face away.

George stood there. He didn't know what to do or say. Then he walked towards the door. He felt uncomfortable and upset. What had he done for this to happen?

Margaret watched him go. George did not know how much she loved him!

When George got home, he thought the house was empty. The phone was ringing, but when he picked it up, there was no one there.

It was strange to be alone and he stood in the hall for some time. He was tired and confused.

When George went upstairs, he found Kay lying down on the bed.

'What's the matter?' George asked. 'Don't you feel well?'

'That girl must be mad!' Kay said. 'Blackmail! Fifty thousand dollars! I've never liked her.'

'Well, it doesn't matter,' George said quickly. 'Where's Arthur Busch?'

'I sent him home.'

'So you're not in love with him?'

Kay looked up at George in surprise.

'In love with him? No, I was drunk. I felt sorry for him and I was angry with you. I thought you realized that.'

George sighed. He was confused. Everything was a muddle. He couldn't think clearly.

'That girl must be mad,' Kay said again.

'Oh, forget it, Kay. She tore up the letters. Everything's all right now.'

'But she'll lose her job, won't she?'

George was horrified.

'Of course not. I don't want her to lose her job. Do you think Margaret believes that? I must phone her! What's her number?'

After some time, someone picked up the phone at Margaret Donovan's apartments.

'Miss Margaret Donovan, please,' George said.

There was a silence.

'I'm afraid Miss Donovan's had an accident,' the person said. 'She's shot herself.'

'Is she … Is she badly hurt?'

'The doctors think she'll be all right. She's in St. Catherine's hospital.'

'Thank you.'

George put down the phone and turned to Kay.

'She's tried to kill herself,' George said. 'I think it's my fault. I must go to the hospital.'

'I don't think you should go there, George.' Kay said quickly. 'People might say …'

'I don't care what people say.'

George went into his room and began to comb his hair. In the mirror, his face looked pale and tired.

'George, I love you,' Kay called from the next room.

'I love you too,' he said.

'Jules Rennard phoned,' Kay went on. 'He talked about going fishing. A few of us could go – men and women. What do you think, George?'

'I don't like the idea much,' George began and then stopped. The phone was ringing downstairs. Dolores, the maid, picked it up.

'Is Mr Hannaford in?' asked a voice.

'No,' Dolores said quickly. She looked at the phone, stuck out her tongue rudely and hung up just as George Hannaford came down the stairs.

'That was Miss Avery,' Dolores said. 'She phones you four or five times a day. I tell her you're out. I don't tell Mrs Hannaford.'

'What?' George stared at the girl. How much did Dolores know about his life?

'Mr Hannaford, I didn't hurt myself this morning, when I fell down,' Dolores said.

'That's fine. Goodnight, Dolores.'

'Goodnight, Mr Hannaford.'

George smiled at her, just for a moment. The magnetism of his smile promised her everything she could ever want.

George walked down the steps to his car. Dolores stood by the door, watching him. There was a strange look on her face.

Was it love or hate? She looked up at the sky, at the thin, pale California moon.

Story: *Three Hours Between Planes*

By F. Scott Fitzgerald, retold by Margaret Tarner

It was a chance, but Donald wanted to take a chance. He hadn't been back to this town for over twenty years. Was she alive? Was she still living here? What was her name now – was she married?

When the plane landed, Donald stepped out into the warm, summer night. He found a phone in the airport building. His heart was beating fast as he opened the phone book and looked for her family's name. Perhaps her father was dead by now.

No, here was his name – Judge Harmon Holmes. Hillside 3194. Donald dialled the number and asked for Miss Nancy Holmes.

'Nancy is married. She's Mrs Walter Gifford now. Who is this speaking?'

Donald hung up quickly. He had found out what he wanted to know and he only had three hours in the town. He looked at the phone book again. Here it was – Walter Gifford, Hillside 1191.

He dialled the number.

'Hello?'

'Hello. Is Mrs Gifford there? This is an old friend of hers.'

'This is Mrs Gifford.'

Did he remember her voice?

'This is Donald Plant,' he said. 'I haven't seen you since I was twelve years old.'

'Oh … Donald! When did you come back to town? Where are you?'

'I'm at the airport … for just a few hours.'

'Well, come and see me!'

'Are you sure it's not too late?'

'No, no. I was just sitting here alone, having a drink. Get a taxi. Tell the driver …'

The taxi stopped and Donald looked at the house. A pretty, dark-haired woman was standing in the open doorway.

In the taxi, Donald repeated every word of their short conversation to himself. He smiled.

The taxi stopped and Donald looked at the house. A pretty, dark-haired woman was standing in the open doorway. She had a drink in her hand. Donald got out of the car.

'Mrs Gifford?'

She turned on a light and stared at him nervously. Then she smiled.

'Donald – it is you. But you look different. We've all changed as we've got older. Oh, it's amazing to see you again!'

As they walked inside the house, Donald felt nervous too. He remembered the last time they had met. She had gone past him on her bicycle, without a word or a smile. Perhaps this visit was an awful mistake. He began to talk quickly.

'You were always lovely,' Donald said. 'But I'm surprised to find you as beautiful as you are.'

The compliment worked. Nancy smiled.

'Would you like a drink?' she asked. 'My husband is away on business. He's just phoned to say he'll be away for another two days. He's very nice, Donald, and very attractive. Rather like you. But I think he has a woman in New York. I'm not sure.'

'That's impossible,' Donald said. 'He can't want a woman in New York when he has a wife like you.'

'I was married for six years and I sometimes thought that my wife was having an affair. Then I decided not to be jealous. After my wife died, I was very pleased that I had made that decision.'

Nancy looked at him kindly.

'I'm very sorry that your wife is dead,' she said. Then, after a moment, she added, 'I remember something my father said about you. He said, "That boy is intelligent." I have always remembered that.'

'What else do you remember about when we were young?' Donald asked, smiling at her.

'Ah, that's not fair,' she said. 'I guess I was a bad girl in those days.'

'No, you weren't a bad girl,' he said. 'I think I will have that drink now.'

'Do you think you were the only girl who was ever kissed?' he went on, as he took his drink.

'Do you enjoy talking like that?' Nancy asked, angrily. Then she smiled.

'Well, we did have fun,' she said. 'Oh, that ride in the snow! Those summers in Frontenac!'

It was the ride in the snow he remembered. He had kissed her cool cheeks, her neck, her eyes, but never her lips.

'And there was that party I couldn't go to, because I was ill,' Donald said, with a smile.

'I don't remember that,' she said.

'Oh, you were there. Someone else kissed you. I was very jealous!'

'It's strange. I don't remember. Perhaps I wanted to forget.'

'But why?' Donald asked with a laugh. 'We were just two young kids. But Nancy, I believe I really loved you then. As much as I loved my wife, later. When my family moved out of town – it was terrible!'

'Were you very upset?'

'Oh God, yes! I —'

He suddenly realized that they were standing very close together. And he was talking as if he loved her now. Nancy looked up at him. Their eyes met.

'Go on,' she said, 'I like listening to you. But I always believed that you loved me. I was more upset than you when you left. Wait a minute, I've got some photographs I want to show you … '

Donald sat on the sofa, thinking about the past. He hadn't felt as confused as this since the death of his wife.

Nancy sat down beside Donald on the sofa and opened the book of photographs.

'Oh, this is such fun!' she said. 'I'm glad you're so nice. I like you even better now. Kiss me!'

'I'm not behaving like a good wife,' she said, after a minute or two. 'I don't think I've kissed another man like that since I got married.'

Donald was excited – and confused. Was this Nancy Holmes who he had known? Or was this a lovely stranger?

'Wouldn't it be awful if we fell in love again?' he said.

'Don't say that!' she cried. 'We shouldn't have kissed. That was a moment I'll have to forget.'

'Kiss me once more,' he said. But Nancy was looking at a photograph.

'Look, there you are!' she said, pointing at the picture.

He looked at the young boy, standing on the beach.

'I remember that day,' Nancy said. 'Kitty took the photograph and I stole it from her.'

Donald looked at the photograph more closely.

Donald looked at the photograph more closely.
'That's not me,' he said.

'That's not me,' he said.

'Oh, yes it is. That photograph was taken on the beach at Frontenac. It was the summer we used to go to the cave.'

'What cave? I was only in Frontenac for three days. I don't remember going to a cave. And that boy isn't me. That's Donald Bowers!'

She stood up quickly.

'Plant! Bowers!' she exclaimed. 'I must be drunk! What have I told you?'

'Nothing at all,' he said, trying to speak calmly.

'You must never tell anyone about when we were kids in Frontenac,' Nancy said in a hard little voice. 'That kind of story gets passed around.'

'Nothing happened. There isn't any story …' He began. Then he understood. So Nancy had been a bad little girl. Suddenly, Donald was jealous – jealous of that other Donald, Donald Bowers.

'Kiss me again, Nancy,' he said. He put his hand on her shoulder, but Nancy turned away.

'You said you had to catch a plane,' she said coldly.

'I don't have to go.'

'Please go,' she said. 'And please try to understand how upset I am.'

'But you are talking to me as though you don't remember me. I'm Donald Plant.'

'I remember you. But everything happened a long time ago. You can phone for a taxi. The number is Crestwood 8484.'

In the taxi, Donald was still very confused. In the plane, he was able to think more clearly. For a few minutes, down there in the town, he had lived in two worlds at once. The boy of twelve and the man of thirty-three had been one person.

In those hours between planes Donald had lost a dream.

But everyone loses their dreams as they get older, Donald thought. It doesn't really matter.

Answer key

1 Impressions

Grammar

1
a) 1
b) 6
c) 4
d) 8
e) 3
f) 2
g) 7
h) 5

2
1 have just bought
2 was walking
3 saw
4 had been looking
5 was selling
6 used to have
7 always feel
8 'm wearing

3
a) So does Venice.
b) So is *Titanic*.
c) Neither has Jodie Foster.
d) So did Daniel Day-Lewis.
e) So has / does Keifer Sutherland.
f) Neither has Antonio Banderas.
g) Neither was Schwarzenegger.
h) So did Tom Hanks.

Sentences c, f and h are completely untrue.

4
a) So do I. / I don't!
b) So have I. / I haven't!
c) So would I. / I wouldn't!
d) Neither do I. / I do!
e) Neither do I. / I do!
f) So am I. / I'm not!
g) So did I. / I didn't!
h) Neither have I. / I have!
i) Neither could I. / I could!

5
a) weren't you   R
b) aren't you   F
c) are you   F
d) do you   R
e) haven't you   R
f) didn't you   F
g) can you   R
h) have you   F
i) did you   F

6
a) hasn't she
b) did I
c) aren't I
d) haven't you
e) was it
f) does she
g) do they
h) shall we

7
a) ✓
b) Do you mind <u>telling</u> me how you met him or her?
c) Could you tell <u>me</u> what your first thoughts were?
d) ✓
e) Do you think that you <u>made</u> a good impression on him or her?
f) Do you know what he or she <u>is</u> doing now?
g) I'd like to know <u>if/whether</u> you still have the same opinion about this person.

8
a) Do you know know what kind of salary you are looking for?
b) Could you tell me which political party you vote for?
c) Do you think that you work well under stress?
d) Do you mind telling me if/ whether you have ever been in trouble with the police?
e) I'd like to know what is more important for you: money or job satisfaction.
f) Would you say that you are a 'morning-person' or an 'afternoon-person'?
g) I'd like to know whether you believe in God.

Pronunciation

a) Speaker A
b) Speaker A
c) Speaker B
d) Speaker B
e) Speaker A
f) Speaker B

Vocabulary

1
Usually positive characteristics:
warm, charming, hearty, sparkling

Usually negative characteristics:
abrasive, fake, harsh, shrill, strident

2
a) 6
b) 5
c) 2
d) 4
e) 1
f) 7
g) 3

3
a) charming
b) hearty
c) impassive
d) forced
e) staring
f) spiky
g) husky
h) designer

4
a) rediscover
b) reunite
c) rebuild
d) reinvent
e) relocate
f) reconsider
g) rewrite
h) ~~reschedule~~

5
a) rearrange
b) reconstruct
c) rethink
d) reword
e) remake
f) redo
g) repackage
h) re-examine

6
a) buckle
b) zip
c) button
d) cuff
e) sleeve
f) belt
g) hem
h) collar

7

a) cuff
b) button
c) collar
d) belt
e) sleeve
f) buckle

8

1 d
2 e
3 a
4 c
5 f
6 b

9

1 guess
2 can't
3 down
4 wind
5 annoying

10

1 that
2 over
3 one
4 with
5 image
6 bears
7 resemblance
8 same
9 recognise
10 looks
11 like
12 looking

Reading

2

The second and the third ads will probably get the most replies.

3

a) 3
b) 2
c) not needed
d) 5
e) 1
f) 4
g) 6

4

appeal / appealing
attract / attractive
entice
tempt

Writing

1

c) A voice and a life

2

1 b
2 c
3 a

3

I first discovered her music because my mother used to like it and listen to it when she was cooking. About ten years ago, Marianne Faithfull was in concert here and we went together. She was superb. I love the way she sings and she has had such a fascinating life. I don't like everything that she has done, but she's always interesting.

4

appeared
beautiful
concert
different
extremely
fascinating
favourite
including
interesting
recently
serious ✓

2 Generations

Grammar

1

a) Lidia decided to <u>study</u> in England.
b) She wanted her parents <u>to</u> pay for her studies.
c) Unfortunately, they could not afford <u>to</u> help her.
d) ✓
e) ✓
f) The family friends didn't ask her <u>to</u> pay any rent.
g) She <u>loved going</u> to classes and she made lots of friends.
h) She spent her free time <u>looking</u> after the friends' children.

2

a) making
b) Let
c) force
d) allow
e) get
f) arrange
g) attempt
h) mind
i) ask

3

a) to understand
b) talking
c) going
d) to help
e) spending
f) to leave
g) know
h) to give

4

a) They couldn't afford to buy lots of new clothes.
b) They encouraged me to go to church every week.
c) They never let me bring friends home.
d) They made me come home at ten o'clock every night.
e) They warned me not to go to discos (because they were dangerous).
f) My father expected me to work in his sock factory.
g) My parents taught me to respect authority.
h) I was dreading telling my parents that I had a boyfriend.
i) I managed to run away from home when I was 15.
j) I tried to live on my own, but it was very hard.

5

1 at
2 to
3 in
4 at
5 for
6 about
7 on
8 to
9 of
10 with

6

a) Do you find it difficult to get up in the morning?
b) Is it embarrassing for you to speak English?
c) Do you find it irritating to get spam emails?
d) Is it easy for you to keep a secret?
e) Do you find it boring to watch adverts on TV?
f) Do you find it amusing to look at old family photos?

Vocabulary

1

1 infancy
2 childhood
3 adolescence
4 adulthood
5 middle age
6 old age

2

a) dreading
b) aiming
c) avoid
d) manage
e) urged
f) warned
g) mind
h) encourage

3

a) Charity begins at home.
b) Blood is thicker than water.
c) Home is where the heart is.
d) Birds of a feather flock together.
e) Two's company, three's a crowd.
f) One good turn deserves another.

4

1 a)
2 f)
3 e)
4 d)
5 c)
6 b)

5

a) impressed
b) fed up
c) irritating
d) hopeless
e) optimistic
f) allergic
g) amazed

6

a) hopeless
b) allergic
c) amazed
d) impressed
e) optimistic
f) irritating
g) fed up

7

1 take
2 call
3 have
4 welcome
5 make
6 show
7 help
8 shout

8

a) very
b) mind
c) Excuse
d) afraid
e) Sorry

Pronunciation

1

a) grey, say, chase, fake
b) buy, try, flight, wild
c) boy, toy, annoy, join
d) go, know, clothes, host
e) how, now, clown, ground
f) their, where, hair, parent
g) hear, near, cheers, serious

2

a) lost
b) wear
c) give
d) low
e) have

Listening

1

a) Speaker 3
b) Speaker 2
c) Speaker 1

2

	Speaker		
topic	1	2	3
boyfriends			✓
entertainment	✓	✓	
fashion	✓		
marriage			✓
money		✓	✓
music	✓		
politics		✓	
studies	✓		✓
work	✓		✓

3

a) a bad job
b) not as good as people claim
c) in a very bad way
d) made very easy for them
e) survive financially
f) a situation where you have two very different advantages

Writing

1

1 d
2 e
3 m
4 n
5 i
6 k
7 c
8 l
9 f
10 g
11 a
12 j
13 b
14 h

2

a) P
b) H
c) H
d) H
e) P
f) H
g) P
h) P

3 Gold

Grammar

1

a) was going
b) would see
c) they had had
d) the next day
e) hadn't finished
f) would love
g) 'd gone
h) we were going

2

a) he had just won
b) he had won; he was going to do
c) he didn't know; he would buy
d) would take
e) he wanted
f) she fancied
g) they were going
h) she was doing

3

a) 'I've got the tickets.'
b) 'Can/Could I see them?'
c) 'When are we leaving?'
d) 'You have (got) two days to get ready.'
e) 'Do I need to take any money?'
f) 'I'll pay for everything.'
g) 'I'm going to buy some new clothes.'
h) 'Do you want to come/go with me?'
i) 'I'll wait for you at home.'

4

a) If I <u>was/were</u> the president of my country, I'd spend more money on the environment.
b) If I <u>ever had</u> the chance, I'd take a year off and go travelling.
c) If I could live anywhere in the world, I'd probably <u>buy</u> a beach villa in Tahiti.
d) If I didn't need to learn English, I would <u>have stopped</u> a long time ago.
e) If I didn't have to go to work tomorrow, I would <u>stay</u> at home.

f) If I had been good at Maths, I would have <u>studied</u> it at university.
g) If I <u>had done</u> more exercise when I was younger, I would be a lot fitter now.
h) If I'd been born with very rich parents, I wouldn't <u>be doing</u> this job.

5

a) 8
b) 2
c) 7
d) 3
e) 6
f) 5
g) 4
h) 1

6

a) If I'd studied harder at school, I'd have a better job.
b) If it was/were made of real gold, it would be worth a lot.
c) If they hadn't cornered the market, they wouldn't have put up the price.
d) If he didn't have a talent for seeing a gap in the market, he wouldn't have made millions.
e) If she had realised it was valuable, she wouldn't have given it away.
f) If my time wasn't /weren't so precious, I would have spoken to them.
g) If I hadn't been working late, I wouldn't have missed the film.
h) If I had known you were coming, I would have come to meet you.

Vocabulary

1

a) office
b) a right
c) a fortune
d) action
e) a risk
f) way

2

a) took
b) make
c) take
d) make; take
e) have
f) having
g) take
h) make

3

a) word
b) action
c) fortune
d) way
e) loss
f) exam
g) look
h) duty

4

a) 5
b) 9
c) 7
d) 6
e) 1
f) 8
g) 10
h) 4
i) 3
j) 2

5

a) Expressions a/5, c/7, d/6
b) Expressions b/9, g/10
c) Expressions e/1, f/8, h/4, i/3, j/2

6

a) a steady stream of people
b) digest the information
c) use your time more profitably
d) food for thought
e) a half-baked idea
f) spare a couple of minutes
g) spent the evening
h) trickling slowly
i) wasting your time
j) worth your while

7

A
1 loaded
2 splash out
3 blow
4 living
5 breadwinner
6 peanuts
7 a rainy day
8 overdraft

B
1 worth
2 made
3 pricey
4 hard
5 range
6 boat
7 budget
8 stretch

8

a) I was looking for something slightly more colourful.
b) I was wondering if you might have something a little less formal.
c) I was thinking of something slightly more exciting.
d) I was hoping for something a little less expensive.
e) I'd like something that looks slightly older.
f) I'd prefer something a little more fun.

Pronunciation

1

a) wealthy
b) whether
c) treasure
d) special
e) stretch
f) deluge

2

a) tʃ
b) dʒ
c) ʒ
d) θ
e) ʃ
f) ð

Reading

1

a) by inventing a meatball-making machine
b) ten years
c) that they can also be successful if they take a few risks and believe in their dreams

2

a) 5
b) 4
c) 6
d) 2
e) 1
f) 3

3

a) F
b) F
c) T
d) T
e) F
f) F
g) F
h) F
i) T

4

a) entrepreneur
b) expert
c) prototype
d) perseverance
e) aired

Writing

1

1 when
2 as soon as
3 While / As
4 then
5 after / as soon as
6 While
7 during
8 As soon as / When
9 until

2

totally – completely
Apparently – it seemed
Suddenly – just then
frantically – desperately
finally – at last

4 Challenge

Grammar

1

a) had always wanted; saw
b) had been preparing; cancelled
c) were getting; rang; told; had stolen
d) had been waiting; had finally arrived; didn't know
e) had never done
f) came; just closed; jumped

2

a) ✓
b) He <u>heard</u> a strange noise behind him.
c) It sounded as if someone <u>was following</u> him.
d) ✓
e) ✓
f) He had never <u>felt</u> so scared in his life.
g) ✓
h) John <u>didn't know</u> what to do.
i) He <u>took</u> one last look over his shoulder.
j) ✓

3

Aron Ralston <u>had</u> been climbing in a remote canyon in Arizona when disaster struck. He <u>was</u> climbing down a particularly narrow part when a huge rock fell and trapped his arm. As he <u>had</u> been climbing on his own, there was no-one to help him. And he knew that no-one would think of looking for him there because he <u>hadn't</u> told anyone where he <u>was</u> going . He <u>hadn't</u> brought his phone with him, so he couldn't call for help. He waited for five long days, but no-one came to find him. By the fifth day he <u>had</u> lost all sensation in his arm. He realised that he had no choice. He

would have to cut his arm off at the elbow in order to save his life. Once he <u>had</u> cut off his arm, he managed to climb to the floor of the canyon. As he <u>was</u> walking out of the canyon, he met a group of people who <u>had</u> been hiking in the area. They called for help and a helicopter soon arrived to take him to a nearby hospital.

4

a) What had Aron been doing when the accident happened?
b) Why hadn't anyone come to look for him?
c) Why hadn't he called for help?
d) How long had he waited in the canyon?
e) What had he done to get away?
f) What had he been doing when he met the hikers?

5

a) He had been climbing in a remote canyon.
b) Because he hadn't told anyone where he was going.
c) Because he hadn't brought his phone with him.
d) He had waited in the canyon for five days.
e) He had cut his arm off.
f) He had been walking out of the canyon.

6

a) have finished
b) be going
c) be working
d) have had
e) have got
f) be going
g) be doing
h) have got; had

7

1 will/'ll be doing
2 will/'ll have started
3 will/'ll have made
4 will/'ll have fallen
5 will/'ll have given up
6 will/'ll be living
7 will/'ll have changed
8 will be running

Pronunciation

1

a) up
b) off
c) down
d) out
e) off
f) after

Vocabulary

1

a) imminent
b) shambolic
c) interest
d) deal
e) genuine
f) obscenely
g) particularly

2

a) self-conscious
b) enjoyable
c) reasonable
d) self-discipline
e) self-esteem
f) accessible
g) self-employed
h) unbearable
i) achievable
j) doable

3

a) self-discipline
b) self-esteem
c) enjoyable
d) doable; achievable
e) unbearable
f) reasonable
g) accessible
h) self-conscious
i) self-employed

4

a) of
b) jammed
c) no
d) out
e) slow
f) load
g) into
h) undo

5

1 figure out
2 undid the zip
3 loaded the gun
4 in charge of
5 no way
6 swung into action
7 it / the gun jammed
8 go into slow motion

6

1 c
2 f
3 d
4 i
5 e
6 g
7 a
8 h
9 b
10 j

7

a) feel
b) picks
c) give
d) lit
e) Look
f) keep
g) come
h) taking

8

a) coming down with
b) putting me off
c) shake it off
d) takes after him
e) let you down
f) get over it
g) look into it
h) do without it

9

a) It's horrible when that happens.
b) It serves you right.
c) You've only got yourself to blame.
d) I'd go home if I were you.
e) You look like death warmed up.

10

1 It's horrible when that happens.
2 You've only got yourself to blame.
3 You look like death warmed up.
4 I'd go home if I were you.
5 It serves you right.

Listening

1

a) To raise the media profile of the wildlife park.
b) The confined space of the cage.
c) No, she doesn't.
d) Yes, she does.

2

a) T
b) F
c) T
d) F
e) F
f) F
g) T
h) T

3

a) do some exercise
b) give someone an idea
c) go for a walk
d) keep fit
e) raise money
f) set a new record

Writing

1

b) Marathons for beginners

2

a) 3
b) 5
c) 1
d) 4
e) 6
f) 2

3

Start by
Try
It's important to
Next you should
It's a good idea to
Remember to
you definitely ought to consider
it's definitely worth trying out
Or maybe you could
Think about
Why not
You just need to
you could always

5 Ritual

Grammar

1

1 find
2 decide
3 clear
4 *not possible*
5 *not possible*
6 do
7 spend
8 *not possible*

3

1 used to
2 didn't use to
3 didn't use to
4 used to
5 used to
6 used to
7 didn't use to
8 used to

4

1 *not possible*
2 wouldn't
3 wouldn't
4 would
5 would
6 would
7 wouldn't
8 *not possible*

5

Suggested answers
a) He used to / would drink beer.
b) He used to have a beard.
c) He used to be a hippy.
d) He'd / would / used to go to discos.
e) He didn't use to drink champagne.
f) He didn't use to be a businessman.
g) He'd / would / used to smoke cigarettes.
h) He'd / would / used to wear his hair in a pony-tail. / He used to have a pony-tail.
i) He didn't use to have a mobile phone.

6

1 used to be
2 would chase
3 found
4 tried
5 would smoke
6 would always get
7 would have to
8 saw
9 had
10 'll / will always pay
11 'll / will have

7

a) Could you remember to lock the door on your way out this morning, please?
b) Do you remember telling me that I was the only person in your life?
c) ✓
d) It's so long ago that I've completely forgotten saying that. Did I really?
e) ✓
f) They stopped for a minute to get some money out at the bank on the way to the cinema.
g) This season, I'm going to try to win both the 100 and 200 metres.
h) Try cooking it in oil – it'll taste a lot better.

Pronunciation

2

a) two
b) nerves
c) bothered
d) mind
e) understand
f) mad

Vocabulary

1

1 jinx
2 striding
3 outfit
4 derive
5 upper hand
6 renowned
7 rituals
8 immune
9 came across
10 loopy

2

a) cosy
b) urge
c) slammed
d) matches
e) first
f) domestic
g) Royal
h) breakneck

3

a) Would you like to have a go on my bike?
b) I'd like to have a go at kite surfing.
c) Did you really drink all that in one go?
d) You've been on the go all day.
e) Why don't you just give it a go?
f) He tried his best to make a go of it.

4

1 f
2 d
3 a
4 e
5 b
6 c

5

1 apt
2 run through
3 gone for
4 walked
5 service
6 happy couple
7 pronounced
8 sunglasses

6

a) ceremony
b) reception
c) honeymoon
d) best man
e) groom
f) speech
g) aisle
h) vow
i) confetti
j) rice
k) cake
l) bridesmaid

7

a) to do
b) to get
c) going
d) visiting /to visit
e) to go
f) being
g) flying
h) to get
i) to do

8

1 complaining
2 insist
3 go
4 keeps
5 on
6 telling

9

a) I hate it when people tell me what to do.
b) It really annoys me when people shout.
c) The thing that annoys me most is a messy desk.
d) I can't stand it when people keep me waiting.
e) I find it irritating when nobody listens to me.
f) Bad manners really get on my nerves.
g) It's so annoying when it rains at the weekend.
h) The way some people drive makes me mad.

Reading

2

a) *Rachel Getting Married, 27 Dresses*
b) *Mamma Mia*
c) *Mamma Mia, Rachel Getting Married*
d) *27 Dresses*
e) *Mamma Mia, 27 Dresses*
f) *27 Dresses*

3

a) 7
b) 2
c) 5
d) 6
e) 3
f) 8
g) 1
h) 4

Writing

1

The correct order is a), c), b), f), d), e), g).

2

a) Further to; in connection with
b) caused directly by
c) over the agreed price
d) in due course
e) furthermore
f) unsuitable for this type of work

3

a legal advice
b a full refund
c the matter
d apology
e I will expect

4

Suggested answer
From most threatening to least threatening: a e b d c

6 Eat

Grammar

1

a) ✓
b) I've always hated
c) I've been a vegetarian
d) ✓
e) I've forgotten
f) I've had
g) ✓
h) ✓

2

a) have/'ve finished
b) have/'ve been cooking
c) have/'ve had
d) has been eating
e) have /'ve probably received
f) have been smoking
g) have/'ve been talking

3

a) She ~~has~~ got the job
b) Cedric hasn't been studying
c) She hasn't told her parents yet.
d) Alyson has been painting
e) he has only ~~saw~~ seen
f) Dan and Ursula have been getting ready

4

1 've been working
2 've been doing
3 started
4 've been paid
5 was paid
6 've been promoted
7 've made
8 've accepted
9 've given
10 've moved

5

1 is eaten
2 eats
3 is usually covered
4 washed down
5 is used
6 means
7 contains
8 needs

6

1 became
2 rose / had risen
3 was made
4 was discovered
5 was greeted
6 were made / had been made

7 was used
8 also ate
9 bought

7

a) I'm being helped with this exercise by a friend.
b) My homework will be marked by my teacher.
c) My dinner is being cooked by my sister this evening.
d) I've never been given a ring.
e) I will not / won't be forced to take an English examination.
f) My dictionary hasn't been opened today.
g) I was invited to a friend's house last weekend.

Pronunciation

1

/s/	/z/
ask	always
beliefs	cheese
extensive	dessert
fussy	invisible
loose	noisy
restaurant	please
this	these

Vocabulary

1

a) 4
b) 6
c) 5
d) 2
e) 3
f) 1

2

a) raised
b) shook
c) stick
d) held
e) bending
f) clenched

3

1 set
2 à la carte
3 vegetarian
4 regional
5 organic
6 dishes
7 paper
8 flavours

4

1 menu
2 dishes
3 light
4 fresh
5 extensive

6 flavour
7 three-course

5

1 The first and most obvious reason
2 In fact
3 As a result
4 What is more
5 Secondly
6 In other words
7 To sum up

6

a) 7
b) 6
c) 3
d) 2
e) 5
f) 4
g) 1

7

1 so
2 Although
3 Furthermore
4 even though
5 Consequently
6 to sum up
7 However

8

a) 1959
b) 0.999
c) 100th
d) 23,302
e) 07/05/2009
f) 020 44 6544
g) 21st

9

a) love; love
b) nil
c) oh
d) oh
e) nought
f) zero

10

chilled menu, overcooked customers, rude service, unhelpful wine

11

a) lemon
b) beetroot
c) pie
d) beans
e) peanuts
f) cookie
g) cheese
h) butter
i) salt

Listening

1

c) Chestnut wins Hamburger Olympics

2

a) 24
b) $20,000
c) eight minutes
d) 85
e) 66
f) peanut butter and toasted cheese
g) hundreds
h) 10,000

3

a) wolfed down
b) swallow
c) get down
d) stuff himself
e) pigging himself
f) tucking in to
g) scoffing

Writing

1

For
it is better for the future of our planet.
organic food is almost certainly better for your health and the health of your children

Against
It is more expensive and more difficult to find
you can't always be sure that it's organic

2

a) to
b) of
c) for
d) of
e) against
f) about

3

a) There are many good reasons
b) some people may disagree
c) We know
d) be a better way of helping the planet
e) What is more
f) It is understandable to

4

a) for
b) for
c) against
d) against
e) against

7 Escape

Grammar

1

a) The travel agent suggested ~~us~~ that we go to Shoreham-by-the-Sea for our next holiday.
b) He assured ~~to~~ us that we would have a wonderful time.
c) He explained ~~us~~ that it had won an award for its clean beaches.
d) He also mentioned ~~us~~ that it had a fantastic nightlife.
e) He convinced ~~to~~ us that it was this year's top destination.
f) Finally, he persuaded ~~to~~ us to book it by offering a discount.
g) The company confirmed ~~us~~ that there would be no price increases.
h) One week before departure, the company announced ~~us~~ that there was a 5% price increase.
i) *correct*

2

a) doing
b) him to be
c) me that
d) that it
e) that she was
f) her to
g) them to

3

a) have to travel / need to travel
b) could only
c) had to book
d) not/n't allowed to
e) were allowed to use / could use
f) couldn't park
g) didn't have/need

4

a) I should have known better.
b) I shouldn't have trusted you.
c) I shouldn't have said that.
d) I'm sorry, I should have told you.
e) It shouldn't have ended like that.
f) I should have stayed at home.

5

a) –; –
b) a; a
c) –; the; the
d) a; the
e) a; –
f) the; a
g) –

6

1 the	11 the	21 The
2 –	12 the	22 a
3 a	13 –	23 –
4 the	14 The	24 the
5 the	15 a	25 –
6 the	16 a	26 the
7 a	17 the	27 the
8 the	18 a	28 a
9 a	19 the	29 the
10 the	20 –	30 the

7

The Holiday
Starring Cameron Diaz, Kate Winslet, Jude Law

Synopsis
A British woman, Iris Simpkins, and **an** American woman, Amanda Woods, are both at **the** end of **a** relationship. They decide to take **a** two-week holiday and go to live in **the** other person's home. They want to forget about men. In **a** small English village, Amanda meets and falls in love with Iris's brother. Meanwhile, in sunny California, Iris meets **a** musician and love is in **the** air there, too.

8

a) You can't measure ~~the~~ happiness.
b) There never was ~~the~~ a good war or bad peace.
c) Friendship is love with ~~the~~ intelligence.
d) Men never remember, but ~~the~~ women never forget.
e) ~~The~~ Money is power.
f) Nothing is certain in ~~the~~ life except ~~the~~ death and taxes.
g) ~~A~~ Time waits for no one.
h) Proverbs rarely contain ~~the~~ wisdom.

Vocabulary

1

a) surveying
b) nibbling
c) towel
d) dinghy
e) sunburn
f) paddling
g) spade

1 surveying
2 sunburn
3 paddling
4 dinghy
5 nibbling
6 towel
7 spade

2

a) suggest
b) advise
c) assure
d) reassure
e) convince
f) persuade
g) mention
h) claim

3

a) claimed
b) assure
c) admit
d) inform
e) persuade
f) confirmed
g) convince
h) insist

4

a) ✓
b) ✓
c) ✓
d) ✓
e) –
f) ✓
g) –
h) –
i) ✓
j) –

5

a) endless
b) careful
c) helpful
d) tasteless
e) relentless
f) doubtful
g) childless
h) stressful

6

a) illegal
b) illiterate
c) impolite
d) immature
e) unwilling
f) illogical
g) undivided

7

1 should
2 well
3 views
4 recommend
5 won't
6 avoid
7 were
8 Whatever
9 must
10 sure
11 place

Reading

1

a) for women
b) to entertain

2

1 b
2 d
3 a
4 g
5 e
6 f
7 c

3

a) 2
b) 1
c) 2
d) 2
e) 1
f) 1
g) 2

Writing

1

Topics mentioned: cost, entertainment, history, sports facilities, language, scenery

2

a) 3
b) 5
c) 4
d) 1
e) 2

8 Attraction

Grammar

1

a) It is thought (that) they have had an argument.
b) It is said (that) they are getting divorced.
c) It is believed (that) an announcement will be made tomorrow.
d) It has been suggested that Frances has taken the children to the South of Spain.
e) It has been said (that) William wants custody of the children.
f) It is believed (that) Frances has fallen in love with a younger man.
g) It is thought (that) they will be getting married in the spring.

2

a) Chocolate is thought to relieve stress.
b) Blondes are believed to have more fun.
c) Grey hair is thought to be attractive in men.
d) Pale skin was said to be a sign of great beauty.
e) Cosmetic surgery was once considered to be an expensive luxury.
f) Brown eyes are believed to be stronger than blue eyes.
g) Working in front of a computer screen is known to be bad for your eyes.

3

a) Get your eyes examined!
b) She is having her portrait painted.
c) We had a spare key made.
d) I must get the car washed.
e) Have you had your photos printed yet?
f) It's time we had the windows cleaned.
g) Could you have my bags sent up to my room?

4

a) I had my eyes tested last week.
b) Why don't you get your shoes repaired?
c) You should get your hair cut.
d) We're going to have this wall knocked down.
e) The company are going to get their logo changed.
f) We had the car checked last week.
g) I want to get my nose straightened.
h) You should get your homework checked.

5

a) How often do you get your hair cut?
b) Have you ever considered having a tattoo done?
c) When was the last time you had your eyes tested?
d) Where do you usually get your photos printed?
e) Have you ever thought about getting your name changed?
f) How often do you have your nails manicured?
g) Where do you usually get your shoes repaired?
h) When was the last time you got a key cut?

6

a) If you **were to find** some money on the street, what would you do with it?
b) Would you have cosmetic surgery, **assuming** you had the money to pay for it?
c) **Imagine** you could make a radical change to your lifestyle, what change would you make?
d) Suppose **someone were to give** you three wishes, what would you wish for?
e) **Supposing** you were to get the chance to spend an evening with the celebrity of your choice, **who would you choose**?
f) What job would you like to do, **assuming** money, time and talent were no object?

Pronunciation

2

a) absent –<u>mind</u>ed
b) <u>big</u>–headed
c) easy- <u>going</u>
d) good-<u>look</u>ing
e) <u>lev</u>el-headed
f) open-<u>mind</u>ed
g) self-<u>cen</u>tred
h) <u>laid</u>–back

Vocabulary

1

a) eye
b) eyebrow
c) cheekbone
d) dimple
e) jaw

2

a) skin
b) teeth
c) eyes
d) jaw
e) smile
f) nose
g) cheekbones
h) eyebrows
i) lips

3

square jaw, upturned nose

4

1 big
2 white
3 full
4 smooth
5 bone
6 high
7 dimples
8 eyebrows
9 eyes

5

a) self-centred
b) grown-up
c) laid-back
d) level-headed
e) open-minded
f) down-to-earth

6

1 self-centred
2 laid-back
3 level-headed
4 open-minded
5 down-to-earth
6 grown-up

7

a) self-centred
b) open-minded
c) grown-up
d) down-to-earth
e) level-headed
f) laid-back

8

a) selfish
b) tolerant
c) mature
d) unpretentious
e) sensible
f) relaxed

9

1 sensitive
2 caring
3 sensible
4 practical
5 trustworthy
6 conventional
7 enigmatic
8 unfriendly
9 dependable

10

a) caring
b) standoffish/unfriendly
c) experienced/mature
d) trustworthy/dependable
e) mysterious
f) straight

11

a) foot
b) ear
c) shoulder
d) chest
e) eyes
f) neck
g) mind
h) fingers

12

1 e
2 a
3 f
4 g
5 b
6 d
7 c
8 h

13

a) did I put my foot in it?
b) get it off my chest
c) made up his mind
d) aren't from this neck of the woods
e) a shoulder to cry on
f) I'm up to my eyes (in work)
g) play it by ear
h) have their fingers in a lot of pies

Listening

1

hobbies, family, tattoos, jewellery

2

a) F
b) F
c) F
d) T
e) F
f) F
g) T
h) T

3

a) 1 I'm only kidding
    2 I'm pulling your leg
b) You're having me on, aren't you?
c) I bet
d) The same goes for
e) Hold on
f) Time's up

Writing

1

George Clooney

2

a) 4
b) 6
c) 7
d) 5
e) 1
f) 3
g) 2

3

a) He looks just like
b) Judging from the way he looks,
c) What strikes me most about him is
d) There is something about him that
e) He looks like a typical
f) At first glance, he appears to
g) He gives an impression of being

9 Genius

Grammar

1

a) must
b) can't
c) might
d) could
e) must
f) may

3

Some people think that the CIA may have <u>killed</u> President Kennedy. They say that Lee Harvey Oswald can't <u>have</u> been responsible for the shooting and the CIA may ~~be~~ have murdered him in prison as a way of stopping the investigation.
A survey in the US found that one in five people think that the Apollo astronauts ~~must~~ <u>may</u> never have landed on the moon. They think that the film of the event must have ~~being~~ <u>been</u> done with trick photography. Some people even believe that the government might have faked all the Apollo missions.
It has been suggested by some people that the US government could ~~has~~ <u>have</u> made secret contact with aliens. A mysterious crash at the Roswell military airport in 1947 may have ~~be~~ <u>been</u> an alien spacecraft. Since then, it is thought that the government may <u>have</u> kept another 11 similar incidents secret.

4

a) I may have made a mistake.
b) You must have been very surprised.
c) I might have seen this film before.
d) She can't have told the truth.
e) I may (not) have paid.
f) He could have already left.

5

a) –
b) like
c) –
d) as if / as though
e) as if / as though
f) like
g) –
h) like

6

a) ✓
b) He appears to be asleep.
c) It seems as if we've been here before.
d) They look like rain clouds.
e) The local people all seemed very friendly.
f) ✓
g) The club looked cool, so we went in.
h) You look as if you've seen a ghost.

7

a) It looks as though it'll rain today.
b) When he is angry he looks bright red.
c) My classmates all seem very friendly.
d) I often look a little tired on Saturday mornings.
e) My kitchen looks as if a tornado has hit it.
f) I often appear to be calm when I'm not.
g) People say that I look like a famous film star.
h) It seems as if my English is improving very fast.

Pronunciation

a) 1 (ii) 2 (i)
b) 1 (i) 2 (ii)
c) 1 (ii) 2 (i)
d) 1 (i) 2 (ii)
e) 1 (i) 2 (ii)

Vocabulary

1

a) shiny
b) run-down
c) contemporary
d) tough
e) eccentric
f) hideous
g) derelict
h) sprawling

2

a) sprawling
b) hideous
c) derelict
d) run-down
e) contemporary
f) eccentric

3

a) main
b) drizzling
c) endured
d) incentive
e) enigmatic
f) mere

4

1 When
2 soon
3 at
4 From
5 Over/During
6 During
7 On
8 Just
9 after
10 while

5

a) 3
b) 1
c) 4
d) 6
e) 2
f) 5

6

1 genetics
2 biology
3 scientist
4 science
5 economist
6 economic
7 mathematical
8 economics
9 physicist
10 mathematician
11 technological

7

1 Insert, Ensure, click
2 Place, clockwise
3 spout, remove, press

8

a) He turned the dial on the thermostat to zero.
b) You can't turn it on until you've plugged it in at the wall.
c) How did people change channels before they invented remote controls?
d) Make sure the lid's on tight before you switch it on.
e) Put a cup under the place where the water comes out and push the blue button, OK?
f) Take the filter out of the holder and replace it after every cup of coffee that you make.

Reading

1

Leonardo painted the *Mona Lisa*, designed tanks and helicopters and studied birds.

2

a) 3
b) 2
c) 4
d) 1

3

Suggested answers
a) Whose workshop did he spend ten years in?
b) Who was Florence at war with?
c) How long did Leonardo spend in Milan (working for Sforza)?
d) When did he become fascinated with flight?
e) How did he spend most of his time at Amboise?
f) How many paintings did he do?

Writing

1 a)

2

California truck driver, Larry Walters **has / had always wanted** to be a pilot

… from a local store and **filled them / had them filled** with helium

By now, he **was panicking.**

An airport helicopter eventually **succeeded** in bringing him back to earth.

3

a) plan
b) (epic) journey
c) purchased
d) seat
e) pistol

4

a) Larry Walters
b) be a pilot
c) join the US Air Force
d) weather balloons
e) weather balloons
f) garden chair
g) seat

5

Suggested answer
At the end of his act, the Argentinian magician, Professor Marvo, asked a male member of the audience who was sitting near the front to come on stage. The magician handed the man a gun and asked him to shoot him in the face. The man fired the gun and the magician then pulled the bullet from between his teeth.

The man was so impressed that he took another gun out of his pocket. While Professor Marvo was preparing to leave the stage, he said to him, 'Catch this!' and shot him. He was killed instantly. Even during the subsequent trial, the man could still not understand why Professor Marvo (had) failed to catch the bullet.

10 Sell

Grammar

1

a) The most expensive advert of all time, which was for the drink Guinness, cost $20 million.

b) It was made by Nicolai Fuglsig, whose other adverts include the Sony Bravia advert.

c) It is thought to be one of the most effective adverts that has ever been made.

d) One of the advertising companies which has had the highest sales worldwide is Dentsu Inc.

e) Castlemaine XXXX ,which is a kind of beer, once showed 17 different TV adverts on one channel in one evening.

f) An advert that was made for British Airways had over 6,000 people in it.

g) The longest advertising poster ever produced, which was made by O'Canada Gear in Alberta, was over 332m long.

h) Eight songs that came from Levi jeans ads have got to number 1 in the British hit parade.

i) Guy Ritchie, who used to be Madonna's husband, has directed a soccer advert for Nike.

j) Nike, which is one of the best known brands worldwide, spent more than $1.7 billion on advertising in one year.

2

a) that
b) who/that
c) who/that
d) that/which
e) that/which
f) whose
g) that/which
h) that/which
i) whose

In **d)**, **e)** and **h)** the relative pronoun can be omitted.

3

a) *Quantum of Solace*, which is the 22nd Bond film, was first released in the UK.

b) Lots of Bond fans who enjoyed Daniel Craig's performance in *Casino Royale* are glad to see him back in the role of 007.

c) Olga Kurylenko plays the role of a Russian-Bolivian agent who helps Bond in his search for revenge.

d) Mathieu Almaric plays the role of the villain who Bond must try to stop.

e) The title of the film is based on a short story which/that appeared in a collection called *For Your Eyes only*.

f) The film is directed by Marc Forster, who also directed the Oscar-winning *Monster's Ball*.

4

Suggested answer

One day, Philip K Wrigley, who was the founder of the famous chewing gum company, was sitting on a plane that was going to Chicago. During the flight, the man who was sitting next to him asked, 'Why do you continue to advertise a chewing gum which is already the most popular in the world?' Wrigley, who was known for his wit, quickly replied, 'For the same reason that the pilot of this plane, which is flying at 30,000 feet in the air, keeps the engine running.'

5

a) 3
b) 1
c) 2
d) 6
e) 5
f) 4

6

a) What I wouldn't want is to be written about in the tabloid papers.

b) It's only in the north of Canada that he's well-known.

c) What I really hate is the way that celebrities always sound so sure of themselves.

d) The only thing that matters to some people is being on TV.

e) What I don't understand is why people take her so seriously.

f) It isn't the soundtrack I don't like, it's the film. / It isn't the film I like, it's the soundtrack.

g) It wasn't John McCain who beat Barack Obama in the presidential election, (but) (it was) Obama who beat McCain.

Vocabulary

1

a) 4
b) 3
c) 2
d) 1
e) 8
f) 7
g) 6
h) 5

2

a) I caught sight of his face for a split second as he walked past

b) ✓

c) I couldn't make out the details in the photograph because the quality was so bad.

d) ✓

e) I gazed at the rain through the window for ages, thinking about what I'd say to her.

f) ✓

g) ✓

h) Sh! They won't notice us if we just stand here and keep quiet.

3

a) confidence
b) tag
c) cut
d) conference
e) image
f) sector

4

a) spending
b) list
c) revenue
d) team
e) name
f) value

5

a) stripped off
b) fussy
c) care less
d) fiercely
e) epitomise
f) rugged; heart-throb
g) nostalgically
h) haunting; conjuring up

6

1 cow
2 back
3 far
4 raking
5 placement
6 office
7 privilege
8 strike
9 clear
10 condition

7

a) I get <u>absolutely nervous</u> before exams. ✗

b) ✓

c) His performance was <u>very extraordinary</u>. ✗

d) That was definitely one of the best films I've ever seen. It was <u>totally good</u>. ✗

e) ✓

f) ✓

g) The film was quite disappointing, but the party afterwards was <u>extremely brilliant</u>. ✗

h) ✓.
i) That was some horror movie. I was <u>very frightened</u> to death. ✗
j) Did you think so? I was <u>extremely bored stiff</u>. ✗

8

1 expectations
2 hype
3 disillusioned
4 waste
5 utter
6 entire
7 complete
8 letdown

Pronunciation

2

a) 2; 1
b) 2; 1
c) 1; 2

Listening

1

1 C
2 D
3 G
4 F
5 E
6 A
7 B

2

a) 3, 5, 7
b) 7
c) 2, 4
d) 3, 7

3

a) 1 Perhaps you could give me a call on my mobile?
   2 Perhaps you could give my secretary a call on 0207 7491 2598.
   3 Could you please call me back there?
   4 Could you give me a call back?
b) 1 I'll try again later.
   2 I'll call again in half an hour,
c) 1 I'm interested in
   2 I'm calling about
   3 I'm looking for

Writing

1

1 Basic information
2 Plot
3 Cast
4 Recommendation

2

a) powerful
b) his performance is worthy of an Oscar
c) one of the best movies I've seen for a long time
d) will appeal to everyone
e) has received rave reviews
d) You won't be disappointed.

3

a) The soundtrack, mostly songs by the brilliant A. R. Rahman, is worth buying on CD.
b) Danny Boyle, the director of the film, also made *The Beach* and *28 Days Later*.
c) As in Boyle's other films, the special effects play an important part.
d) Based on a novel by Vikas Swarup, the screenplay was written by Simon Beaufoy, the writer of *The Full Monty*.
e) The ending, which is no surprise, is the stuff of fairy tales.
f) 'Hollywood melodrama,' said one critic, but the film is much more than that.

11 Student

Grammar

1

a) will do
b) going to fail; don't
c) are coming
d) has started; will be
e) Will anyone try
f) might
g) are going to have; are
h) 'm going to wait; know

2

a) until the exams have finished
b) I'll have finished
c) I look
d) finishes / has finished
e) unless the weather changes
f) I will probably have spent
g) don't give

Pronunciation

1

a) list
b) feel
c) book
d) soon
e) head
f) learn
g) course
h) fan
i) buzz
j) heart
k) want

2

a) /e/
b) /iː/
c) /ɜː/
d) /æ/
e) /ʊ/
f) /ɑː/
g) /ɒ/
h) /ʌ/
i) /uː/
j) /ɔː/
k) /ɪ/

Vocabulary

1

1 pay
2 heart
3 marks
4 further
5 failed
6 course
7 applied
8 grant

2

a) It is unlikely (that) he will study very hard .
b) It is likely (that) he will fail most of his exams.
c) He's bound to turn up without a pen.
d) It's inevitable that he'll try and cheat.
e) It's probable (that) he'll end up at the bottom of the class.
f) He's not expected to go on to university.
g) It's unlikely (that) he'll get a good job.
h) He's bound to get into trouble with the police.

3

a) taste
b) behind
c) system
d) senses
e) make
f) up to her

4

a) mind-blowing; amazing
b) mind; worried
c) moon; happy
d) legs; exhausted
e) burst; sad
f) tether; desperate
g) breath; amazed
h) dying; thirsty
i) door; ill
j) stiff; afraid

Reading

1

1 b
2 b
3 a

4 b

2

a) Maths and English. Children.
b) Yes.
c) Yes. Because he feels he makes a difference.

3

a) 4
b) 8
c) 2
d) 5
e) 10
f) 6
g) 1
h) 9
i) 3
j) 7

Writing

1

1	a	(F)	n	(I)
2	b	(I)	g	(F)
3	c	(I)	f	(F)
4	d	(F)	j	(I)
5	e	(F)	m	(I)
6	h	(I)	i	(F)
7	k	(F)	l	(I)

2

Part 1 a), i)
Part 2 d), f), k)
Part 3 e)
Part 4 g)

3

I was born in a small village not far from Eindhoven, so my mother tongue is Dutch, but I have a good standard of spoken and written English, because I have been going to an excellent language school near my town and I have been to America four times in my holidays. I also had an Irish girlfriend for a couple of weeks. I have an international driving licence and I currently drive a red convertible Audi. I was going to work for a travel company here in the Netherlands last year, but in the end I worked for two months at the help desk at Schiphol Airport, where I had to deal with people from all over the world, and sometimes I got to drive one of the airport buggies if there was a disabled passenger who needed some help. It was great fun.

12 Home

Grammar

1

a) overlooking
b) walking
c) taken
d) watching
e) cleaned
f) read
g) located

2

1 Sitting
2 going
3 occupying
4 admired
5 Fitted
6 specializing
7 known

3

1 many
2 several
3 few
4 no
5 plenty
6 little
7 hardly
8 most
9 enough
10 None
11 all

4

a) of
b) not
c) ✓
d) ✓
e) of (second)
f) ✓
g) ✓
h) the
i) the (second)
j) ✓

Vocabulary

1

a) pop next door
b) fossil fuels
c) central heating
d) street cred
e) fireworks display
f) pitch dark

2

1 e
2 f
3 h
4 j
5 b
6 g
7 d
8 a
9 i
10 c

3

1 Well, I'd better be going. It was really good to see you.
2 Good to see you, too. Thanks for coming.
3 My pleasure. Thank you for inviting me.
4 Give me a ring some time, OK?
5 I will. Give my regards to Betty, will you? Bye.

4

a) cellar
b) loft, utility
c) porch
d) dustpan, brush, mop
e) parquet, tiles, fitted
f) doormat
g) blinds
h) glazing
i) sill
j) bolt
k) mantelpiece, ornaments
l) hook, peg
m) point

Listening

1

a) New homes / residential properties
b) about 800
c) four
d) They have high walls and security cameras. They are guarded by dogs and armed security personnel.
e) 26 million dollars

2

a) T
b) F
c) F
d) F
e) T
f) F

3

a) crammed
b) link-ups
c) hippest
d) not short of a buck or two
e) armed

Writing

1

a) 2
b) 4
c) 3
d) 1

2

There are many possible answers.